A Mountain Township

EDWARD
SANBORN

A
MOUNTAIN
TOWNSHIP

BY

WALTER HARD

WITH AN INTRODUCTION BY
DOROTHY CANFIELD FISHER

STEPHEN DAYE PRESS

NEW YORK

*Illustrations for the new edition by
Edward Sanborn
Illustration for "The Village" by
Raymond Bishop*

LIBRARY OF CONGRESS CATALOG CARD NO. 62-22261

PRINTED IN THE UNITED STATES OF AMERICA

To Madison C. Bates,
a friend

Acknowledgments are made to the *Manchester Journal* and the *Rutland Herald* for the use of various poems, many of which first appeared in their pages.

Contents

IN THE VILLAGE

Introduction

YOU will remember, I am sure (that is, if anybody
nowadays remembers such things), that Goldsmith
took care never to reveal what the story of the grouse
in the gun-room really was. All we know about it is
that at its every repetition it grew more irresistible to
those who had been brought up on it. As I turn over
the pages of this book in which Walter Hard has set
down with unobtrusive art the old stories on which we
Bennington County Vermonters were all brought up,
I wonder for a faint-hearted moment whether perhaps
Goldsmith was not right. What will sophisticated mod-
erns make out of this covey of old-time grouse from
the Vermont gun-room?

These stories of earlier generations of our families
and their neighbors, many of them dead before our
parents were born, whose personalities—strange or com-
monplace, weak or vital, frail, mean, sweet, eccentric,
lovable, absurd—were handed down to us in talk, along
with our Windsor chairs and patchwork quilts; these
flashes of frankly rustic humor—gay as in "An Uphill
Courtship," grim as in "A Joy Ride," grisly as in "Pa
is Hindered," dryly sardonic as in "Waitin' "; these
light-hearted senseless grotesques as in "The Jailbird"
and "Spring Haircut"; this occasional home-grown,
astringent reticent poetry as in "The Old Captain,"
"When Grandma Went Away," and "Plowing Time"
—how will they look, I ask myself uneasily, to book-
educated city and suburban people? It is a little like

taking one's beloved but rustic, eccentric, humorous, and altogether grand old great-aunt out to a metropolitan party.

Walter Hard's is a curious case, perhaps one calling for the research of folk-lore and folk-way experts, so naturally, spontaneously and unportentously does he work; almost as if still living in the golden age before authors had heard about the various labeled pigeon-holes into which creative writing must be thrust. A cultivated, college-bred man, he persists in claiming the privilege of primitive folk to write what they are moved to write. He has been moved to set down in a form of his own invention, a body of folk-talk that has been accumulating for a century and a half in a little corner of the States where people have the habit of staying put. Asked insistently, as he often is, by serious-minded critics if he considers his work as "poetry" he only laughs. Questioned—perhaps with some impatience—by a self-appointed judge used to more formally literary writers, "But if you won't claim that it is poetry, why print it in short lines as if it were?" he answered with perfect sincerity, "Because I think, if I do, people will read it more as I mean it." Informed severely by a doctrinaire of verse, "*I* can't see the faintest trace of rhythm in your work," he remarks good-naturedly, "Can't you? I can." Adding perhaps, as he looks with meditative eyes past his interlocutor at the irregular, unexpected but flexible and never-broken lines of our Vermont landscape, "It's a kind of Vermont rhythm, you see."

To see him amusedly parrying passes with sophisticated people is rather fun. What is delightful is to see him with a Vermont audience gathered of a winter evening in a Town Hall to hear him read. None of them arrives brandishing unrestfully a handful of labels. The audience has come from far through the snow looking for what they get, an invitation to reflect—deeply, mirthfully, sadly, bitterly, contentedly—on human life as they know it. They have come to hear their own stories told with a rhythm and an intonation that bring out their meaning as a stone is cut to bring out its color. They will be reminded in a folk-tongue that is theirs by right of inheritance that human nature is sometimes laughably wrong-headed as in "Church Union"; sometimes silently grand (they would not admit it if it were not silently so) as in "An Officer of the Town," and in "Holy Night"; they will burst into laughter at familiar sharp digs at their own weaknesses as in "Sabbath Keeping" and "Fitting the Shoe" and "A Hero Returns"; they will be shown a gallery of portraits painted with the skill that makes a good portrait an interpretation of the subject— "Scat," "A Health Note," "A Test Pilot"—to confirm them in their native habit of nourishing their hearts and minds by sucking the savory marrow of significance out of the fact-bones of everyday life and everyday people.

For they are everyday. Vermonters are mountaineers, yes, but not Celtic or picturesque ones. There is but a very faint occasional trace of Paul Bunyanism or of Mark Twain extravagance in the stories with which they make their comments on human life. Rigorous understatement rather than exuberant overstatement is their native idiom. Their poetry is implicit. Their passion is too concentrated an essence to dilute with many words. Read "An Empty House" if you would hear the language which seems to them the fit one for expressing the ineffable—either of rage or joy. Above all they are Anglo-Saxons in ruling out self-pity from among the permissible emotions. In their code it is too far beneath contempt to deserve expression; and, as every reader of lyrics will admit, if you rule out self-pity, a very large part of—at least of romantic—poetry goes with it.

But what remains is not flat, toneless and stale as the articulate self-pitiers would naturally think. In this compendious guide to Vermont ways of looking at life, there is, in addition to self-pity, one other emotion you will not find expressed. This is boredom. It does not thrive in the Vermont climate, kept down as it is by the necessity to work hard, and by the habit (common to most mature human beings *when the daily routine of their lives leaves them time for reflection*) of trying to extract from each particular which comes into personal life some light about the general of which it is a manifestation.

To make this statement thus categorically turns it at once into an exaggeration, almost a falsification of the facts. But I can't think of a better way to call to your attention the philosophic quality of a good deal of the material which Walter Hard has here collected and re-told. Whether it is in a livery stable ("The Liveryman") or thinking about the death of an old horse

("On Dying") the tendency of the Vermonter—although he would not recognize it, baldly described in these terms—is to try to see how the isolated detail that comes before his eyes in the daily round is related to larger matters. For us "A Connoisseur" is not merely an amusing cartoon of one individual grotesque. It is felt and used in talk as a satiric comment on the unavowed content of the familiar masculine cant-phrase "Oh, I don't think women should be too intellectual!" This is of course nothing confined to Vermont, but simply the way in which all folk-stories have been used, from Æsop's on, by the simple folk who have picked them out of the chance happenings of daily life and saved them to use as comments on human nature.

The mention of ennui suggests a warning about how to use this volume which may be necessary for readers not familiar with the like. You will be wise to bear in mind that the separate items in this book really do not belong together, should (if the nature of things had been followed as it never is in civilized life) not have been gathered up into one collection. It was not thus that we heard them told us by our elders. We hope you will take care to read them as they were told, one at a time, with an interval of living in between. In real life they are brought out only when some happening needs a comment to bring out its significance. Do you incautiously reveal the condescension of the stable and permanent for the rootless stranger? "You and Ella Wheeler!" says your great-aunt dryly, and you hear the story Walter Hard has deftly set down in "A Newcomer." Does a well-tailored summer resident assume in speaking to you that certain condescension felt by city for country? "Remember what Martin Colton said Mr. Peterson was?" asks an old man as the urban visitor moves away.

But of course the reminders in real life of these significant stories occur only once in a while. In setting down in black and white this folk-stuff of ours, polished and worn smooth by much handling, Walter Hard has taken a risk, has put them at the mercy of gluttonous, over-hasty readers. They lose their savor if read too many at one sitting, as fatally as do pancakes when too large a pile are put away at one breakfast.

Well, let them go then, out into the world that knew them not in real life. Hail and farewell, Great-grandmother Hawley, and Great-uncle Zadok, and old Cousin Pamela and Grandfather Canfield's hired man, and Aunt Mary Hard's minister and the French Canuck who worked for Uncle Harmon in the shop. Their bones lie in one or another of our old burying grounds; safe in our memories and our talk are the drop or two of essence of wisdom or foolishness or fun or tragedy or nobility or weakness which each distilled from what life brought to him.

Who ever would have thought to see them in a book!

DOROTHY CANFIELD FISHER

Arlington, Vermont

I

IN THE VILLAGE

The Village

There. From this hill look down.
That's the village.
It's like a man lying flat on his back.
The wide village street is the body.
There's an arm stretched to the east
And one lower down to the west.
Those two converging roads
Are the legs spread wide apart.
Where the head ought to be the figure fails,
Unless you make those wandering roads
Wisps of hair waving in the breeze.

There it lies
Dozing peacefully under the maples—
A church, a school, a tavern, some stores,
And a matter of fifty houses.
Somebody's hammering off to the south,
Probably mending fence.
You can hear the ring of the anvil
In the blacksmith's shop over there,
Where smoke is coming from the forge chimney.

The clock in the steeple strikes five.
The sound is a part of the stillness.

A flock of doves circles up from the road
Where a scuffling horse draws a buggy,
Kicking up a small cloud of dust.
The doves light on the Court House roof.
In a minute they are back in the road.

The East Mountain is hazy and seems far away.
It stretches as far as you can see north and south.
The winding river with the brush-lined banks
Shows silver patches here and there.

A sleepy village in a peaceful valley.
Yet, friend, there life stages its drama.
Tragedy, comedy; nobility beside self-seeking;
Petty crimes against the spirit;
The wise serenity of old age;
The rebellious passion of youth.
There the whole of life unfolds
From childhood's carefree days
To that hillside with the white stones.
Fifty houses offering the life of the race.

Calm twilight settles on the valley.
The birds are singing their evening song.
Come. It's time to go down.

Rural Free Delivery

Frank had been the R.F.D. man for so long
That the younger generation knew no other.
Probably he knew more about each family on his route
Than anybody around except perhaps Dr. Mosely.
In fact, Frank treated his patrons
Much as the Doctor did his patients.
He was never in too much of a hurry or too tired
To lend a hand whenever it was needed.
He'd helped put out fires and built them for sick folks.
He'd assisted at the birth of numerous farm animals
And twice he'd help usher a baby into the world.
That was the ultimate in rural free delivery.
The time Henry Scuttle and his wife were both down sick
Frank looked after the stock on his regular morning trip
And then went over again after his afternoon one.

But it wasn't so much the innumerable physical aids he gave
So much as the tonic for the spirit he dispensed.
No matter how tough the day or the going
He made it the butt of a joke.
When his patrons had troubles to complain about
He always listened with a sympathetic ear,
And then, by the time he left, they felt brighter.
Once in a while, in winter, he had to leave his car
And make part of his trip on snowshoes.
He'd have a good mile to go to get to the Elton place,
And even though there was just a newspaper to deliver
He'd get that there and do it cheerfully.

One spring the roads had been about impassable.
The bottom seemed to have dropped out
And stayed that way for days at a time.
Frank stopped at the Grant place.
His radiator was sending up a cloud of steam
And his wheels were dripping mud.
"How's the road?" old man Grant asked from the wood-
    pile.
"Oh, it ain't bad," Frank said,
"S' long as you stay on top."

The Doctor

The large house under the elm is the Doctor's.
In the ell to the north, on a glass door,
You'll see the word OFFICE in gold letters.
Inside there is a bookcase full of bottles.
There's a worn couch near the window
Next to the disorderly desk with a bracket lamp over it.
There is smell of medicines in the room.

When the Doctor is out Mrs. Stevens tends office.
Sometimes she dispenses pills; sometimes, advice.
Frequently she does some emergency dressing
And quiets a frightened mother until the doctor comes.

There are five horses in the big barn out back.
Many days the Doctor uses them all.
Perhaps he has a call up Beartown way.
The snow is deep and the road just a track.
He finds the going too hard for the horse,
So he ties him to a tree and plows on on foot.

He stamps his snow-covered feet on the kitchen porch.
A man whose face is lined and serious
Holds a lamp high over his head at the door.
The Doctor takes off his buffalo coat
And warms his hands over the kitchen stove.
All the time he talks quietly with the man.
He walks into the bedroom.
He meets the frightened look of the woman
With a smile of encouragement

That smile is his first treatment.
He sits on the side of the bed
With his gold watch in his hand,
While the fluttering pulse tells him the story.

A lighted lantern stands on his back porch.
No matter how late it is, Mrs. Stevens is waiting.
She has something hot on the stove.
She tells him Sam Elder has been there for him.
He drinks the steaming soup slowly.
Then he takes his buffalo coat and the lantern.
He gives his wife a pat as he starts for the barn.
He harnesses another horse
And sets out under the winter stars.

He gets home just in time for breakfast.
The two boys have milked the cow
And fed the horses, so he has no chores to do.
After he's had his second cup of coffee,
He looks at his wife and smiles his quiet healing smile.
"Well, Molly, they've got another nice boy
At Sam's," he says.

A Newcomer

One of the reasons Ella Wheeler fought
To keep that hedge around the burying ground
Was that it had always been there.
As time went on she came to believe
That her father had helped set it out.
That made another argument for keeping it.
What if it did look dilapidated.
They could set out some new bushes
To replace the dead ones.

For some years the Village Improvement Society
Had wanted to replace the hedge with a white fence.
They had straightened the toppling stones
And cut the grass and made the inside look so well
That they thought it should show from the street.
Each time it came up, Ella mustered her forces
And outvoted the modernizers.

Doctor Stevens was the new president of the Improvement
   Society.
He'd been practicing in the village for thirty years.
He had always been in favor of the hedge removal.
He brought the matter up at an early meeting.
Ella had the matter laid on the table.

Two weeks later there was a full meeting.
Ella had all her cohorts in line
And as usual the motion to remove the hedge was lost.
This time, however, Ella won by only three votes.

She was talking about it after the meeting.
Her face was still red with the excitement of battle
And she talked in a high-pitched voice.
"It ain't that I'm so sot on savin' that hedge,
Though heaven knows Father worked hard enough set-
tin' it;
What I object to more'n anythin' else
Is havin' a NEWCOMER like Doctor Stevens a-comin' in
And tellin' us what we'd ought to do.
Land sakes, he ain't lived here more'n thirty years."

No Reservations

Lottie Smike had married young
And gone out West with her husband.
The rest of the family stayed on the old place
Reasonably contented to get along
No matter how few worldly goods they had.
Lottie had always said she wasn't going
To work all her life with nothing to show for it.
She picked wisely when she married
And worked hard with her husband the first years.
He had gathered a very comfortable bank account
By the time he was killed in a train wreck.

After that Aunt Lottie came back every summer
For a long visit at the old home.
The front room was kept for her especially
And it had to be in apple pie order.
The rest of the house was not so carefully kept
What with children, nieces and nephews of Aunt Lottie,
Running all over the place.
As years went on Aunt Lottie grew richer
Due to the prudent investing of her husband.
The more she had the more she worried.
She was forever looking ahead
And usually missing any pleasure the present offered.
She'd no sooner get to the farm
Than she'd begin to worry about getting back West.
She always had reservations weeks ahead
For the train and at hotels in places she planned to visit.

She never could get used to the happy-go-lucky ways
Her relatives seemed to enjoy.

Then one autumn a week before she planned to leave
She failed to respond when they called her for breakfast.
She never recovered consciousness.
A day or so later one of the nieces,
Who had come home as soon as word had come
Of Aunt Lottie's death,
Was talking with some of the family
About the great suddenness of Aunt Lottie's going.
Finally she stopped in the middle of sentence.
She looked startled for a minute and then said:
"Good heavens! She couldn't have had time
To make any reservations."

The Night Watchman

Night after night,
Year after year,
He had made his rounds.
Now he was getting old.
He walked slowly
And he used a cane.
Each evening he came down the street
Carrying his lantern
And his tin lunch-pail—going on duty.
His eyes were blue and calm
And they had an answering twinkle.
Unassuming, patient, uncomplaining,
Through quiet summer nights,
Through dark winter nights
When the wind drifted the snow.
He made his hourly rounds.

Then one day he was too feeble to go.
His eyes were bright
But his legs refused to move.
A new man took his place.

He never knew he was a hero;
But a small boy used to waken
And listen to the wind roaring up the valley
Driving the snow against the tight shut windows.
Then he'd think of the old watchman
Out there in the cold alone.
He'd pull the covers over his head

And snuggle down into his warm bed,
Wondering if some day
He would grow up to be brave too,
And walk alone in the dark and storm
Like old Charlie Millett,
With just a cane and a lantern—
Not even an air rifle
To protect himself from robbers.

The Parson

Next to the meeting house, under the elms,
Stands the parsonage where Parson Blake
Lives with his wife and daughter.
They moved to the village nearly fifty years ago,
When Eliza, the daughter, was a baby.

In his early days the parson had a black beard.
He spoke familiarly of heaven.
He told of a certainty who the sinners were.
With equal assurance he foretold their doom.
As a shepherd he easily separated the sheep from the goats.

As the years went on his hair grew white.
He became less sure in his attitude toward sinners.
He came to find many of them had pleasant virtues.
One day he went fishing with the town drunkard.
From then on his wife and Eliza found it necessary
To keep constantly before his eyes the dire necessity
Of keeping oneself unspotted from the world.
They even feared his mind might be giving way.
Probably it was.

His sermons were filled with the old phrases.
In fact he never thought of a change in theology.
It all came over him so gradually.
He was held by his training and the historic church.
He was also held by the close attention
Of his wife and daughter there in the front seat.
His real sermons were lived during the week.
Many of his congregation never came inside the church.

You'll see him now puttering around his garden.
His hair is long and his shoulders are bent.
His face is that of a dweller in another world.
His fair skin has the translucence of fine marble.
Something within shines through.
Children like to stop at the picket fence.

Men out in the world remember nights in his study
When the Greek grammar was put aside and there was
    high talk.
On hill farms, where life is hard,
His visits are treasured memories.

Day by day he has achieved his immortality.

Socialized Medicine

Dr. Mosely had been practicing in the valley
Since the days he'd had to keep horses
To get around in winter and in spring mud time.
As the roads got better and he could use a car
All the year around the Doctor used the saved time
Not to make more visits but to make them longer.
Answering a call he'd fulfill his professional duties
Usually with dispatch and always with skill.
Then he might sit and talk with the patient
And probably with some other members of the family.
He might go over local affairs and often
He'd go out into the kitchen and have a cup of coffee.
Perhaps he didn't realize it but just this social visit
Normalized many a household and so relieved anxiety
And the strangeness that sickness often brings.
Or he might stroll out to the barnyard
And, leaning on the fence, talk about stock
Or even politics with the menfolks.

Then the time came when the Doctor had to slow up
And he welcomed a young man who gradually took over.
He was strictly professional in his bearing,
Friendly and pleasant but not inclined to visit.
One day Mrs. Glode was doing some spring cleaning
For Mrs. Stillman in the village, and the new Doctor drove
    past.
Grandma Stillman was sitting by the window knitting.
She spoke well of the new young man.

"But I do miss the real friendly calls of Doctor Mosely,"
  she said.
"Why, he might sit and talk over old times for a half hour."
Mrs. Glode stopped to wring out her cleaning cloth.
"Yes," she said, "I kinda feel that way, too.
I've heard 'em talkin' on the radio .
'Bout this new idee, they call it new, in medicine.
And even if Truman and the Democrats are fur it,
I like this social medicine,
Jest as you do."

Church Union

Perhaps when the town had been younger
There had been enough church goers
To support three churches.
Even then one would have been enough.
For some time one had been quite vigorous.
The other two were just kept alive
By a few families in whom habit or hate was strong.
There had been talk of joining the two weaker ones
But always one man in each church
Had blocked it.

Parson Thomas was a young man.
He had been asked to preach
In one of the struggling churches,
Which was just then without a minister.
He knew the situation in the town
And he decided this was a heaven-sent chance
To sow good seed.
So he prepared a sermon on Unity.
He developed his theme carefully.
At the end he made his application
To conditions right there in the village.
He closed with a direct plea.

Deacon Godfrey, the mainstay of the church,
Came hobbling down the aisle.
He tucked his cane under his arm
And shook hands with Parson Thomas.
"A powerful discourse, young man."

He repeated it.
"A powerful discourse."
Then he seemed to be reminded of his duty.
He spoke rapidly as though he feared
He might be weakening.
"Mebbe what you say 'bout church union
Has somethin' to it.
But just let me tell you one thing,"
His voice rose to a falsetto,
"You, nor nobody else,
Ain't agoin' to unite me."

Sabbath Keeping

Mrs. Sleeper had undergone
What was professionally known
As a "conviction of sin" when she was young.
She had grown into a tall angular woman
With a set smile made up largely of teeth.
Her smile was not any evidence of a sense of humor.
She simply used it to temper her justice with mercy.
That she had a perfect right
To pass judgment on her neighbor's conduct,
She never doubted.
Her religion gave her a set of rules
From which any deviation meant sin.
There was nothing in her code
Which said anything about sins of the spirit.
If her husband did not have a very happy life
She knew it was because he did not obey her laws.
If he would not reform he should suffer.
He did, in silence.
He found consolation in his dog
And his days of hunting in the woods.

Mary Powers lived next door.
She tried to live peaceably with her neighbor,
But she didn't take any stock in her beliefs.
She even tried to make life more bearable
For Sam Sleeper when Mrs. Sleeper didn't know it.

One Sunday afternoon another neighbor dropped in
To see Mary Powers.

She found her in her sitting room.
The shades on the windows next to the Sleepers'
Were all drawn down.
Mary sat there sewing on a rag rug.
"My lands, Mary," said the neighbor,
"Why are you sittin' here on a bright day
Sewin' with all the shades drawn?"
Mary smiled.
"Well, you see, I had to get this rug done
So it would get to sister Sary day after tomorrer.
That's her birthday."
She threaded her needle.
"I knew the Lord'd understand
My workin' on the Sabbath,
But I want so sure of Mis' Sleeper."

The Choir Visible

Ever since the Meeting House was built
The singers had stood by the organ
In the high balcony
At the back of the church.
It was generally understood
That they should be heard
And not seen.
There were usually eight singers.
Then there was George Swallow
Who played the cornet.
Some of the older members
Were never quite sure
That a band instrument was proper in church.

Some changes were being made
In the interior of the building
And some of the younger group
Urged that the organ and choir
Be moved up in front by the pulpit.
The change was proposed at a meeting,
And met with a strong opposition.

One Sunday the services were held
Downstairs in the Lecture Room.
The choir sat in front by the melodeon,
Facing the audience.
Mrs. Williams, who was nearsighted,
Leaned forward to see
Who was in the choir that morning.

23

She had been sick so she hadn't attended the meeting
When the change in choir location was discussed.
After looking the singers over
She turned to the woman next to her
And whispered, whistling on all her s's:
"I hear they's some talk
Of movin' the singers up front, upstairs."
Her neighbor nodded.
"Wal, come to look 'em over,
I'm agin it."

Hunger Strike

Zeke Gifford was the valley's professional hired man.
He'd worked at one time or another
At almost all of the farms in the region.
His quick temper was usually the cause of his movings.
But he was such a good worker
And had such a way with him handling cattle
That he was never out of work for long.
He was often rehired where a year or so before
He'd left in a huff or been fired
When he'd lost his temper over some little thing.

His chief claim to fame
Was his capabilities at the table.
He was slender, wiry, and quick in his motions.
Where he managed to stow away all he ate
And what became of it was never evident
By any additions of fat to his slight body.
Folks had learned that his eating habits
Were one thing they must not joke about.
Glances might pass among the youngsters at table
But Zeke must never know that anybody had an idea
That his appetite was anything but normal.

One morning he drove into the creamery.
He was evidently in a bad humor
From the way he slammed the milk cans around.
He'd only been working for Widow Collins a few weeks
But he'd let it be known that his stay there
Might not be very long.

Somebody asked him, this morning,
How things were going at the Widow's.
He leaned over a can with his hands on the handles.
"I'm sick of that woman," he said.
Then he squinted as if to focus on something special.
"You know what she sez t' me this mornin'?"
He didn't wait for any suggestions but went right on.
"She sez t' me, she sez, 'Do you know
How many griddle cakes you've et a'ready?' she sez.
'You've et eleven by count' she sez."
He lifted the can onto the rack.
"I was so damned mad," he went on,
"I got up and come away without m' breakfast."

Knowing Beans

Marcia Haskins was ambitious.
She wanted office for Abner.
He was perfectly willing
To let others have the glory—
And do the work.
His indifference prodded his wife to greater efforts.

She had been encouraged that spring
When he'd been elected Tree Warden.
His name loomed just as large
In the paper's account of Town Meeting
As Mrs. Thompson's husband's,
Even if he was a Selectman.

Having secured a civil office
Marcia decided to run Abner for Deacon.
She made a thorough canvass
Of the members of her church,
But when the Clerk read the result of the ballot
His last words were:
"Abner Haskins, three votes."

Marcia had somehow got her things on.
She gathered up the pans she had brought
Filled with baked beans for the supper
And swept out of the door.
On the way she managed to express her mind
To one or two who sat near.
Abner followed her out.
He looked bewildered.

The next morning Marcia threw a shawl over her head
And hurried over to Sarah Petty's.
She didn't stop to wash the dishes.
Sarah had not been to the meeting.
She belonged to another fold.
Marcia broke the news of the election at once.
"Do you know, Sary Petty,
How they pick out a Deacon in that church?"
Sarah, pleased to find another denomination at fault,
Encouraged the revelation.
"Well, they set the candidates in a row
Just under the edge of the balcony."
She leaned forward to illustrate.
"Then they drop beans onto their heads.
If the beans bounce off they don't want 'em.
But, if they SINK IN, Sary Petty,
THAT MAN'S ELECTED."

The Milkman

That house with a cow in the yard
Belongs to Ellery Whitcomb and his wife.
Perhaps it should be Mrs. Whitcomb and her husband.
Some years ago Ellery had a mind of his own.
That was before he married Henrietta.

Ellery used to be the milkman.
His farm was two miles out on the valley road.
For thirty years he hardly missed a day.
Winter and summer he'd come up the street
With the milk cans clattering.
He had just two buggies during those thirty years.
When you came near you could be sure
They'd been associated with milk for some time.

Ellery had a big bell which he rang to warn those
Who had forgotten to put their pails out.
Often the customers would come out with pitchers
Into which Ellery ladled the milk from the can.
These patrons also got the morning news.
He had a pint cup soldered to a long tin handle.
He'd usually dip three times for a quart
Though the last dip was more a matter of form.
On the dashboard he had a tin box.
He dropped the tickets through the slot in the top.
The customers usually bought twenty red tickets.
These meant a quart of milk each.
The yellow tickets meant pints.

When the flies were bad and the horse swished his tail
It often passed over the open milk can.
People didn't mind a few hairs in those days.
Men wore them on their chins.

One day Ellery's son drove the milk wagon.
Ellery had been taken to Brattleboro.
He had been acting strangely for some time.
After a while his wife sold the farm.
Some folks said it was because she nagged him
To sell the farm that he lost his mind.
She moved to that place over there with the cow in the
    yard.

Now Ellery is back, but not back home.
The farm will always be his home.
He keeps that one cow and putters with a garden.
He wanders around with his head bowed.
He has a strange look in his eyes.

When you speak to him of the old days
He may try to talk and then he'll begin to cry.
Perhaps he remembers that he was then
A man of importance in the village.
He'd carried the milk for thirty years
And hardly missed a day.

A Hero Returns

The usual crowd was standing around
Waiting for the evening train to pull in.
The two bread boxes from the store
Were occupied by three of the old-timers.
They knew those boxes wouldn't go out
Until the next day on the nine fifteen.
A whistle sounded to the north.
One of the sitters on the bread box pulled out his watch.
"She's a mite late," he said.
The man next examined his timepiece.
He questioned the accuracy of the other's time.
The third one had his time server in hand by then.
They were still arguing as to which watch was right
When the train drifted down toward the station.

George Stone threw a mail bag into the car
And stopped to talk with the mail clerk.
As the train started he picked up a thin bag
And walked slowly toward a sagging surrey.
Old Kate stood there with bowed head
Apparently fast asleep.
Except for an occasional stamping of a foot
Or listless swishing of her tail,
She'd seemed to sleep most of the time.

George found a passenger in the back seat.
He was tall and had the appearance of a city man.
He greeted George, who answered with a glance and a
  grunt.

31

The passenger was Henry Stebbins.

He'd left town years before, a poor boy.

He was returning fairly well off and famous.

He'd just been appointed to a high governmental position.

"Don't know me do you, George?"

He asked as they started toward the village.

"Yep," George answered. "You're Hen Stebbins."

After a period of silence Henry tried again.

"Well, you know I've moved up in the world."

George slapped Kate with the reins.

"So I heard."

"Well, the boys must have been surprised when they
heard."

"Yep," said George. "They was."

"Well," Henry persisted, "what'd they say

When they got the news of my appointment?"

George pulled on the reins and clucked to Kate.

"Nothin'— Jest laffed," he said.

An Officer of the Town

For more than forty years
The Captain had held some office in the town.
Two years after he was invalided home—
He always suffered with that shoulder—
They made him Sheriff.
For twelve hard years he carried out the court's decrees.
Refusing another term as Sheriff
They made him a Selectman
And for eighteen years he filled that office.
Then, because the Overseer of the Poor
Had let things get in a bad way,
They persuaded him to take that thankless job.
He held it until a year before he died,
Doing his best to save the voters money
And let no deserving family suffer.
Of course he was hated by the shiftless
Who wouldn't save when they had work,
And wouldn't work when they had a cent left.
They spread tales of his heartlessness.
Enough of the voters knew his worth
To elect him each year.
Few ever thought to thank him.

Town meeting was in session.
The regular business had been done
When the Moderator rapped again for order.
"Gentlemen," he said,
"Captain Dever lies on a bed of pain
From which he probably will never rise.

For many years he has been your servant:
Efficient, faithful, honest.
I suggest that the voters here assembled
Rise, and stand, in silence,
A slight tribute to a man."

They rose and stood in silence
And by that silence said
What they had felt for years,
But never told the Captain.

And while they stood he died.

The Abandoned House

You'd hardly know there was any house
Back of that tangle of brush.
From this side you can see the gable end
And the fan window, and part of the chimney.
It belongs to Philip Dewey.
He sends a check every year from South Dakota
To pay the taxes on it.
He never has allowed any repairs.

From the hill at the back you can see better.
From there the main part shows
And you can see why once it was one
Of the show places in the village.
Now most of the windows are broken.
A blue curtain hangs out of one upper room.
The yard is a tangle of lilacs, rose bushes, and trees.
You'd never know there had been a well-worn path
Leading to a hospitable door.

Philip and his wife had been married eighteen years
When she fell sick with a malady the doctors couldn't cure.
Philip gave up his store and devoted all his time to her.
Some people thought he was trying to make up
For the way he'd acted some years back,
When he went around with a girl
Who worked on the Hildreth place.
Anyway, he gave his wife everything he had
During the three years of her sickness.

The day after the funeral Philip took a small valise
And put in it a few of his wife's choicest things.
Without saying good-by to anyone except the station agent,
He left for South Dakota, where his married daughter
    lived.
He's seventy-odd now and very feeble.
He'll never come home again.

In her room in the house things are just as they were.
Her clothes hang in the closet.
The table with the medicine bottles on it
Stands by her bed, and a glass
With a butter pad over it.
Her bonnet, the one she wore the last time she walked,
Hangs on the hatrack in the hall, where she hung it.
And dust streaks out to meet the morning sun,
And cobwebs tremble in the evening breeze.

A Cheerful Walk

It had rained all night—
A gentle warm rain.
The morning air was washed and clear.
A soft wind swayed the branches of the maples.
Along the village street
Women in sunbonnets were bending over flower beds.
Back on the hills the farmers were plowing.
The whole valley had come to life
After months of waiting.

Silas Bent walked slowly up the street.
He stopped to chat with his neighbors,
Leaning on the fence to rest.
Silas had been sick most of the winter.
He looked thin and pale
And he walked slowly.
He felt left behind
With all the busy life around him.
He seemed to sense for the first time
That he was old—too old to be of much use.

He sat down on the bench in front of the Court House.

He took off his hat and wiped the sweat from his face.
Someone came along and stopped to greet him.
He told them of his sickness
And how tired he felt.
They tried to cheer him up
And told him how he'd be working in his garden

Before long.
He brightened up at the thought of his garden.
He recalled that he did feel stronger some days.
"Yes," he said, "some mornings I feel pretty smart."
He sat up a little straighter.
"Last week, one morning, I felt like walking.
I felt real pert like,
And I walk'd t' the cem'try."

At the Court House

Down the rough mountain road
The man, silent, drove the rattling Ford,
Seeing only the road ahead.
Through the weary days of the trial
He, silent, had looked ahead.

The mother sat on the back seat.
She kept saying over and over:
"He never done it . . . He never done it."
All of the familiar beauty of the cool June morning,
The perfume of the mountain woods,
But added to her woe.
"He never done it . . . He never done it."

A crowd stood about the Court House door,
Laughing, talking.
"Nope. Been out all night.
No verdict yet.
Tough case."

The bell had rung.
Slowly the careworn jurors,
Unshaved, tired-eyed, serious,
Filed into the courtroom.
The Sheriff brought in the prisoner—
Her boy.
"O God, he never done it!"

"Deserved all he got."
"Shh. That's his folks."

Slowly the creaking car
Crept back up the mountain.
At the clearing on the summit
They could see the broad valley,
The mountains to the east
A peaceful green in the light of the setting sun.
But in their valley the sun had set.

Nothing But the Truth

Her face was red
And her hair had escaped
From the tight morning knot
At the back.
Her hat, of a style long past,
Had slipped back on her head.

At first she hadn't been able
To find her voice.
Under the kindly guidance
Of her father's lawyer
She had finally told her story—
At least she had told that part of it
The lawyer wished the jury to know.

Under cross-examination by the other side
She had become bewildered
And then she'd lost her temper.
When she stepped down from the stand
She had proved a strong witness
For the opposition.

With several other witnesses
She was sitting on the north side of the Court House
Eating cookies from a bag.
Her father came around the corner
With his lawyer, who was speaking
In very emphatic tones.
"I told you to tell her

What she was to testify to.
Now she's lost us the case."
He scratched a match viciously.

Her father took off his seedy black hat
And scratched his head deliberately.
"B' gol, Mr. Archer,
I told her all I knew."
He turned to the lawyer
With a gesture of despair,
"And then she didn't know nothin'."

A Pride Humbler

Jesse, Noble, and Belus were brothers.
The first two were God-fearing men
Who occupied respected positions in the village.
Belus was different.
Everybody—almost everybody—liked him.
Children were always his friends
And every dog in town gave him a wag.

But Belus was fond of strong drink.
He'd come home one afternoon in winter
When his sister was entertaining
The Ladies Sewing Circle in her parlor.
Belus was feeling in a sociable mood
And before his sister knew it
He was in the midst of the Sewing Circle.
To him it seemed to be a revolving circle.
"Why, Brother Belus, what ever is the matter?
You must be sick.
I never saw you like this before in my life."
Belus finally located his sister.
"Now, Shister, what makes y' shay that?
Seen me like thish thousan' times."

The next day Jesse and Noble called upon Belus.
They informed him that they had been shocked
At his conduct before the Sewing Circle.
They proceeded to admonish him.
They pointed out the position they occupied
In the eyes of the village.

"Brother Belus," Jesse asked,
"Why do you persist in your wicked ways?"
Belus looked out of the window a minute.
Then he turned on them both.
"I do it jest to humble your damned pride.
That's why."

A Chronic Invalid

That small house on the lane, back of the Tavern,
Is a tenant house belonging to Caleb Saunders.
Tom Fitch and his ailing wife have lived there
For nearly ten years now.
Tom helps Caleb around the Tavern.
He's never been able to pay much rent.

Tom's wife was a sister of Rose Cabot.
Nobody ever understood how she and Tom
Ever came to be married.
The story was that Tom had been on a spree—
He did drink a good deal in his youth—
And when he was sobering off
Effie Cabot took him to a revival meeting.
Whatever happened, about that time they were married
And Tom hasn't touched a drop since.

Effie has had something wrong with her heart
Or her stomach or some part of her anatomy
Ever since she has been married.
Tom has to do all of the housework
And what little he can earn around the Tavern
Largely goes to pay for the newest thing
In patent cures Effie has happened to read about.
She generally stays in bed all winter.
She is apt to improve with the weather in spring.
By summer she is able to sit out.
You'll find her on the porch over there
With a shawl around her shoulders

And a bottle of something and a spoon on a stand,
Where she can reach it each hour.

One morning when Tom was about worn out
With waiting on her,
Somebody in the Post Office asked how she was.
"Oh, she's jest about the same," Tom said in a tired voice.
"I wisht she'd git well," he paused and sighed,
"Or sumthin'."

The Milliner

Perhaps you've noticed that small house
With two or three hats hanging in the window.
That's where Mary Smeddy lives.
She's the milliner and those hats in the parlor window
Are some she's made for customers.
She likes to have them left a while after they are done.
She'd hardly call it advertising.

If you pass in the evening she'll be sitting there
By that south window in the sitting room.
She may hold a bonnet up to see how that flower looks.
She jumps up frequently and disappears.
She has gone into the back parlor
Where her invalid sister, Susan, lies on a couch.
Mary is a slave to her sister.
She buys oranges for her every week.
She gives her the tenderloin
And eats what's left in the kitchen.
Much of her money goes to buy medicines for Susan.

When she was young Susan was the pet of the family.
When Mary was helping her mother
Susan was out on the street dressed in her best clothes.
When Rob Peters stopped going with her
She assumed an air of jaunty indifference.
As the days went on and he did not come back
She grew thin and pale.
On the day he was married she took to her bed,
And Rob has children in school now.

Once a neighbor was sure she saw Susan
Walking past Rob's house.
It was a night Mary was at prayer meeting.
Probably it wasn't Susan.
This person was all bundled up so you couldn't tell.
And then Susan had to be helped
Even to get from her bedroom to the back parlor.

Mary will go on slaving for Susan
Who has a broken heart.
No one will know that Mary
Loved Rob Peters.

The Carpenter

Phineas Norton is the village carpenter.
You would never know it
Judging by the appearance of his house.
It looks as though he had never had time
To finish it.
That pile of lumber in the yard
Will be completely overgrown in another year.
Phineas himself doesn't look quite finished.
He is loose-jointed and angular.
He moves quickly.
He likes to see how fast he can do things.
He can never stop for the finishing details.

When Phineas was young he was sickly.
He worked out a system of exercises
And they say he keeps them up even now.
He likes to show you how he can put his palms
Flat on the floor without bending his knees.
He's taught his three boys to wrestle
But only the eldest can win a throw from him.

He is very religious
But he never goes to any of the churches.
There is no sect he can agree with.
In politics he cannot fit into any party.
He sees things in the large.
When it comes to practical details
He always disagrees.
He has never stopped to finish his ideas.

Folks have learned never to argue with him.
If he wants to put a window
Where they'd planned a door,
They usually let him do it.

Last Christmas he worked a week
In his shop there, back of the house.
He wouldn't even tell his wife
What he was about.
On Christmas morning the little Osgood girl,
The one who lives in that tumbled-down house
On the back road by the river,
Found a doll house just outside her back door.
It was big enough for her to get inside.

Phineas isn't a very good workman
But in some ways he carries on the tradition
Established by a carpenter many years ago.

No Change

He'd been a big man in his day, McGuffey had;
Powerful and rich,
The author of ponderous platitudes.
He said nothing in such high-sounding phrases
That he was known as an orator.
He had made himself and he advertised the product
With such sureness
That the thoughtless called him great.
Strangely nature had made a dwelling
Fit for a statesman or a king,
But poor McGuffey could ill support it.

Judge Flagler had a brain
Fit to dwell in old McGuffey's body.
Almost too honest to be kind,
And yet to misery so kind
He'd even cheat his mistress,
Her Majesty, the Law.
"That crook McGuffey," the Judge would growl.
He remembered things which other folks forgot.

And now, still with the bearing of a man of parts,
McGuffey wandered up and down the street
With a queer uncertain gait,
Going somewhere but never getting there.
His little light had flickered out
And left the lamp.

The Judge, sitting in his office door,
Puffing his brown church-warden pipe,

Observed with unrelenting scorn
The approach of McGuffey and his alert attendant.
Taking out his pipe
The Judge spat viciously upon the ground.
Then he said:
"Here comes old man McGuffey.
He *always was* a damned old fool
And *now* they say he's losing his mind."

An Empty House

That house next to the Parsonage is empty.
It's been empty ever since Zadok Haywood bought it.
Now they say he's offering it for sale.
It seems too bad when he and his wife
Had set so much store on getting off the farm
And spending their last days near the church.

They'd both worked hard and saved.
They planned to rent the farm
When they moved into the new house.
The year they bought it Artemis,
Zadok's younger brother, who lived in New York,
Sent a special delivery letter.
He had gone to New York some years before.
He was a handsome fellow
And had never felt he belonged on a farm.
He'd married a girl from a fine family
And seemed to be very prosperous.

It was never known just what the letter said.
The story was that Artemis had got himself
Into a bad scrape, and had to have money.
So Zadok drew from the bank
The money he'd saved for a few years
Of easier living.
Of course Artemis was not the kind
To think of sacrificing to pay it back.
So Zadok is offering this village place for sale.
He'll have to go on slaving on the farm
For the rest of his days.

Artemis was up for a few days last summer.
He looked as young as he did the day he left.
He was carefully dressed and straight as an arrow.
He was walking with Zadok to the barn one day.
"Z," he said, throwing back his shoulders,
"You look like an old man. You're all stooped over."
Zadok changed hands with the heavy pail.
Artemis went on talking.
"Why don't you stand erect the way I do?"

Zadok set the pail down.
He remembered the house in the village
And the days of leisure that would never be his.
He looked at Artemis.
He picked up the pail
And went on toward the barn.

The Postmaster

That building near the Tavern
Is the Postmaster's house.
The Post Office is in what used to be the parlor.
Henry and his wife need only the sitting-room
Since the children have grown up.
Henry has been Postmaster
Since a few years after the war;
Except during the Cleveland administrations.

As a representative of the government
Henry takes his position seriously.
Strangers, looking through the small window
In the middle of the case of a hundred boxes,
Would see a man with a thin face, a graying beard.
They would be struck by the black eyes
Which looked over small gold-bowed spectacles.
They'd probably notice Henry's derby hat
And the unlit Trojan cigar in his mouth.
The hat and cigar, Henry feels,
Befit the office he fills.
He smokes a pipe for comfort.

To the office comes the village.
It offers, twice a day, the exciting possibility
That something unforeseen may happen.
It has the lure of a gambling place.
Through it connection is made with the world.
Henry knows when the store-keeper gets a letter
From that worthless brother who had to go West.

He knows who sends out of town for things,
And probably what the postal cards say.

Yes, and Henry knows why the Doctor's daughter
Always manages to get the Monday afternoon mail.
When he hands her the letter from New York
He smiles a little, and she blushes.
After she has slipped the letter inside her waist
And gone out, Henry puts his hands into his pockets
And hums a little tune.

Perhaps that evening in the sitting-room
Henry's wife will say:
"Land sakes, Henry, what you thinkin' on?
You've set there with a far-away look
The last ten minutes."
Henry will pick his paper up hastily.
"Well, I see they've hed another crop failure
Out in th' Middle West," he'll say.

The Landlord

That's the Tavern, with its fluted columns
Rising from marble flagstones to the porch roof.
Back of the small desk, in the office,
You'll find Caleb Saunders sitting with his feet up.
In the corner there's a chunk stove
Which glows in winter and glowers in summer.

Caleb and his wife came from over the mountain.
Two of the children have married and moved away.
Hattie, the youngest, helps her mother.
They say Hattie looks just as her mother did
Before her face got so wrinkled.
Caleb always manages to dress well.
There are no signs of care on his face.
If it hadn't been for Ma Saunders' hard work
The mortgage would never have been paid off.

When the stage from Bennington rolls up
Caleb is always at the door.
He calls old Pete to take the bags.
He likes to give Pete orders.
Caleb makes a great show as a host,
But the neat bedroom with the sweet-smelling linen
And the well-cooked supper in the dining room—
With these Caleb has had nothing to do.

Every night except Sunday,
Caleb plays euchre with his cronies in the office.
A busy man has to have some relaxation.

57

While Ma Saunders and Hattie are finishing in the kitchen,
And seeing that the rooms are ready for the night,
Caleb, in the office, is telling how hard he works.

If Ma Saunders notices Caleb's failings,
Not a word of it ever passes her lips.
Hattie's slight attempts at rebellion
Are always put down by her mother's calm eyes.
But inside of Hattie's mind a determination
As to the kind of man she'll marry is growing firmer.
She's sure the new schoolmaster who boards there
Would never let HIS wife—
But that's another story.

The Liveryman

Back of the Tavern there's a long red barn.
That's Jim Peterson's livery stable.
Jim lives across the street with his wife and daughters,
But you'll usually find him at the stable.
Now and then Jim swaps horses.
He always has two or three "he might let go."
But most of his horses are members of his family.
He never lets a careless driver have one a second time.
He keeps them until they're ready to stop work.
Then he puts them out on a farm.

You'll find Jim sitting in his small office.
On the walls there are fly-specked prints
Of famous trotters of the past.
Nell J., drawing a high-wheeled sulky.
The driver wears a gay-colored blazer and cap.
Nell's record is given below.
Then there's a faded photograph in an oak frame.
That's Jim's older daughter when she was three.
She's sitting on Clara Belle's broad back.
Now Jim likes to see his daughter driving Clara Belle's
    son.
He keeps a red-wheeled buggy for her special use.
One of the Doctor's sons likes to see her too.

When Jim and his wife drive out they use the roans.
Mrs. Peterson looks almost as young as her daughters
And Jim's ruddy face belies his years.

Jim says, for the ordinary man,
A gentle, steady, all-around horse is best.
But now and then he finds a piece of horseflesh
That's good for just one thing—speed.
He may be ornery, nervous, and unreliable
But just as a speedster he's worth owning.
"You have t' put up with all his cussedness
Jest because he's meant fer one thing in life.
In human critters they call it 'genius'!"

A Jailbird

The jail was a comfortable sort of place,
With plenty of light and air.
It was under the same roof as the Tavern.
The Tavern keeper was the jailor.
The inmates were fed from the Tavern.

Shorty Hall had been in jail so long
That only a few remembered why he was there.
He'd never committed any serious crime
But it seemed easier for the authorities
To have him kept there.
He went out whenever he wanted to in daytime.
He did odd jobs around the village.
He earned enough for all his expenses,
Such as tobacco and raiment.

He was a good fiddle player
And he played at dances sometimes.
On those nights he did not have to come in
To be locked up at ten o'clock.

One fall he got careless.
He got in the habit of going to a farm
Three miles down the road,
Where the cider was just right.
He'd been late getting back several times
And Ed Hubert, the Tavern keeper and jailor,
Had warned him each time.
Then one Saturday night he was later than ever.

Ed was waiting for him when he came in.
"Look a'here, Shorty, I've set up fer you
Jest one too many nights,
Waitin' t'lock you in."
Shorty stood blinking in the bright light,
After his long walk in the dark.
"First thing you know," Ed continued,
"You'll come back some night
And find yourself locked out
Of this jail, by judast."

Spring Haircut

It was getting along toward spring.
There had been several warm days in succession
And there was some talk of sugaring.
Town Meeting was only a few weeks off
And John Vanderlip decided it would be safe
For him to have his hair cut.
He let it grow through the winter
So he wouldn't catch cold.

He found the barber alone.
He was trying a razor he'd been honing.
It was Judge Pettibone's razor
And the barber was splitting a hair with it.
Judge Pettibone and splitting hairs
Brought up the subject of Town Meeting.
While the winter's crop was harvested
All of the town affairs were gone over.

The barber shook out the blue sheet
And let John out of the chair.
John went up to the mirror
While the barber went to the back
To get the broom and dust pan.

When the barber turned around
John was getting into the chair again.
He looked at him with open mouth.
"Wal, young man," John said severely,
"You've just got to cut it all over.
'Tain't in no ways right.
You've cut it too darn short."

A New Change

During the winter there was a dance
Each Thursday evening
In the hall over Saunders' Tavern.
Old and young were there.
There were children, parents, and grandparents.
A professor came up from Troy by train
To teach the beginners.
Johnny Peters played the fiddle
And his daughter played the melodeon.
The dancers balanced corners, saluted,
And swung their partners until they were dizzy.
Money Musk, Scotch Reels, and that mad orgy,
The Tempest.
There were a few stately waltzes.

One night the dance wound up as usual
With the Tempest.
Faster and faster Johnny's bow
Scraped across the squeaking strings.
The old melodeon got out of breath
Trying to keep up. It wheezed and missed.
The dancers whirled madly.

Suddenly there was a heavy thud,
Wild shrieks and a deep groan.
John Vanderlip had turned too short a corner
And his one hundred and ninety-odd pounds
Had struck the floor in a heap.

He was telling about it the next day.
"Yep, I learnt a new change last night."
He rubbed the seat of his pants gingerly.
"Yep, I learnt to change ends."

A Thorn-hedged Garden

Down that road to the left
You'll find a house set in a garden.
A high thorn hedge shuts it off from the street.

If you look through the hedge
Perhaps you'll see a sun bonnet
Bobbing up and down among the flowers.
Under it you'll find Mrs. Ballard.
Mr. Ballard, her second husband, is a quiet man.
His mouth is a straight line.
He appears to be keeping many things to himself.
He runs a small tin-shop back of the Court House.

While Mrs. Ballard is legally wed to Mr. Ballard
She seems to live much of the time
With Hiram Williams her first husband.
Mr. Ballard knows that Hiram was a perfect mate.
It is to mow Hiram's grave that Mr. Ballard
Goes through the street each summer Saturday
With a scythe and rake over his shoulder.

On Memorial Sunday Hiram's favorite chair
Stands flag-draped in the church vestibule.
Mr. Ballard placed it there early in the morning.

Perhaps if you stop at her gate to talk
Mrs. Ballard will show you her flowers.
Probably she'll pick a bouquet for you.
Then she may lead you to her vine-covered porch.

Somehow she'll bring Hiram in.
He enlisted in '61.
Yes, there'll be tears; the story has thrived on tears.
Then, as you get up to go, there'll be some verses.
Sad, sad verses. How she enjoys them.

Out of a past that was hard and unhappy
She's made a paradise with a hero in uniform.
Out of a real and comfortable present
She makes a drab background for her shining past.

And Mr. Ballard's mouth shuts tighter and tighter.

Interference

Samuel Hickok was always busy.
He walked fast
With his head in front of his feet
As though his mind worked faster
Then his lagging body.
The trouble with Sam was
That he was busy
About other folks' business
Nine out of every ten hours.
When you saw him hurrying along
Apparently deep in serious thought,
He was probably transporting
A choice bit of village gossip
To the back room of the shoe-shop.
He was so busy telling his neighbors
How to carry on their places
That his wife did most of the work
That was done on their few acres.

Sam was leaning on the picket fence
Giving Jim Newcomb advice
About his garden,
When young Higgins drove past
With a new team of Western horses.
He had driven them up and down the road
Several times, evidently showing them off,
When Sam stepped out and stopped him.
He looked the team over
With a knowing eye.

Then he said to Higgins
In a very businesslike manner:
"Jest ez I thought, and was tellin' Jim here,"
He jerked a thumb in Jim's direction,
"That nigh mare interferes."

Young Higgins pulled on the reins.
"Wal, thank the Lord, Sam Hickok,
She don't interfere
With nothin' but herself."

Martha

Beyond the blacksmith's there's a house
Weather-beaten and shabby.
The gate of the tipping picket fence
Hangs by one hinge.
The yard is a tangle of lilacs and wild rose bushes.
That's where Martha Powell lives.

Years ago she went to college.
Then because she thought her father needed her
She gave up her college and came home.
She taught school in the village.
Her father raised vegetables and peddled them.
Martha still keeps the old cart in her barn.
When he found Martha could support him
He gave up peddling and spent his time fishing.

Martha did baking for the summer people.
She made rugs too.
She did anything to get more things for her father's com-
   fort.
Then she gave up her school so he shouldn't be alone.

After her father died folks said:
"Now Martha will have a little rest."
Two weeks after the funeral she went to York state.
She brought back a small niece, six years old.
Her sister's family was having such a hard time.

Martha tried to give her niece
All of the things she'd planned to have for herself.

She got a parlor organ and had Mrs. Burt
Give her music lessons.
That she wasn't any more musical than her aunt
Didn't make any difference.

The few little triumphs the child won
Were grand triumphs for Martha.
She always found excuses for her many failures.
Some day she should go to college.
At last she was ready to graduate from High School.
Martha spent almost her last penny for her dress.

When she ran away that summer and got married
Martha's disappointment was almost obliterated
By the romantic atmosphere of an elopement.
Romance had never come so near before.

And now Martha, gray and careworn,
Is full of plans for little Martha,
Her niece's youngest child.
She's making them as she sits there on her porch
Sewing on a rug.
She closes her eyes to rest them.
A tired old lady sleeps in her chair.

The Storekeeper

That small house with the dormer windows
Belongs to Eben Sedgwick, the storekeeper.
Eben really lives in his store on the corner.
You'll find him sitting on a stool
Posting his books on the high desk.
When the sun comes in through the window
It shimmers on a gauze of cobwebs.

Eben is short and he's getting heavy.
His hair is thin and white
But his beard is quite dark.
When he comes to wait on a customer
He always has a smile around his eyes.
Perhaps May Simpson, the dressmaker, wants buttons.
Eben will turn to a disorderly array of boxes.
He'll look over his glasses and sing: "Buttons, buttons."
Probably before May goes out Eben will suggest
Some lone man who needs a button sewer.

On the other side there are groceries.
Barrels of beans, corn meal, sugar—brown or white;
And of course one of fat Boston crackers.
Two cheeses, one mild and one strong,
Stand on the counter by the scales.
There's a barrel of kerosene by a cask of molasses.
A strange smell comes from the sawdust on the floor.

Then there's a counter with some store clothes on it.
In a wall case there is a shelf of lamps
And a pile of black hats such as Eben always wears.

Eben has never made more than a living.
Probably he isn't much of a merchant.
He is much more than a merchant.
Of course he's sung in the choir
And been school committeeman for years.
He's always on some board or the head of some committee.
But many of the things he does are only known to a few.

When he dies his executor will say harsh things
About many of the accounts on his books.
Eben knew he'd never get his pay
But he just had to help out
When there was so much trouble in the family.
But the things that never appear on books!
What a ledgerful Eben would have had!
Little kindnesses, a cheering word,
Advice, sugar-coated with a story.
Just a smile.

When Eben passes on
Some may wonder at the few dollars in the bank.
None will be surprised
At the number of his friends.

Nervousness

Rob had come to the village
To get his week's supplies.
His team of black oxen
Yoked to a two-wheel cart
Stood with heads down in front of the store.

Rob lived near the top of the mountain
On the old turnpike.
There, in the old days,
Stagecoaches used to cross
Carrying mail and passengers to Brattleboro.
Now the road was just a single track
Through the thick woods
Which more and more encroached on it.
Here and there a cellar hole
Or a house with broken windows
And sagging roof
Showed where mountain farms had been.
Rob was the only one left.
He still lived on his place
And in summer had a few campers
Who used some of the rooms in the old house.

A horse trade was being talked over
By some of the sitters in the store.
Rob listened a while
And then when he had an opening
He began to describe a real horse.
She was a black mare

74

And she'd been the pride of Rob's life.
"She want no sort o' hoss fer women t' handle.
Not that there was anythin' out about her
But she was high-strung and nervous-like."
Rob pointed out of the window.
"Wal, she was keyed up all th' time
Jest like that nigh ox out there."
In his peaceful valley
An ox might be a symbol of nervousness.

Seven Dollars

John Ferber inherited a body
Which held its own with the other men—
And the shopworkers were a hardy lot.
But John inherited from a French grandmother
Something the rest didn't have.
Sometimes·music would rouse it.
Sometimes the sun setting across the mill pond.

One of the men had complained to the foreman
That he'd lost seven dollars
From his vest hung up in the shop.
(He found it in the coat pocket at home that night.)
The new foreman found John had been there alone
During the noon hour.
John protested his innocence.
Even the men seemed to doubt him.
When they found the money
It seemed to make no difference to John.
He brooded over it day after day.
They'd believed he was a thief.

Slowly he stood up and shook his head.
He felt in all of his pockets.
He turned them inside out.
He stepped back and held out his open hands
To show that they were empty.
The keeper closed the door.

Seven dollars.

Plowed Fields

The barns were filled with hay;
The corn was in the shock
Waiting for the husking bee.
It was warm in the middle of the day
But as soon as the sun dropped behind the mountain
There was a chill in the air.
Children were making a leaf house
In the yard next to the village store.
There was something waiting in the air.
The season's work was done.

Silas and Henry were sitting in the sun
On the steps of the store.
They were both in the seventies.
They'd both given up their farms
And were living in the village.
The younger ones could do the farm work now.

There was a plow on the store piazza.
The storekeeper hadn't been able to get rid of it.
Its handles and share were painted green and red.

Silas and Henry had been reminiscing.
They talked of the crops they'd grown.
Henry told again about the bay colt he'd raised.
He never tired of telling of her virtues.
Silas was a cattleman and his talk was of good milkers.

They fell silent for a time,
Each one busy with his memories,

Memories of days that would never come again.
Finally Silas looked up at the plow.
"Many's the mile I've walked behind one o' them."
He sighed regretfully.
Henry tapped the step with his cane.
"Yes," he said, "and if I was ever
To walk another mile
I'd as lief hev one of them t' lean on."

A Base Deceiver

Miles had walked most of the way
Through the deep snow from Winhall.
He stamped his feet
At the door of Robert Ames' store
At Factory Point.
He pressed the latch quietly,
Opened the door just enough to squeeze in,
And then let the latch drop carefully.
His manner was always unobtrusive.
He walked over to the big base-burner
Which stood at the back of the store.
Mr. Ames looked up from his books
And said, "Hwarye,"
In reply to Miles' soft-spoken greeting.

Miles removed his cap and mittens
And unwound the tippet from his neck.
He sat down in the black wood arm-chair
And took off his moccasin rubbers.
Placing his cold feet on the bottom of the stove
He settled back in expectation of warmth and comfort.

Shortly after Miles arose.
He had put on his moccasin rubbers
And was winding his tippet around his neck.
He approached Mr. Ames.
"I suppose, Mr. Ames," he said,
"Those new-fangled stoves
That get fed from above

Are supposed to be wonderful."
He was pulling his cap over his ears.
"But when it comes to warmin' my feet,
I'd jest as soon think of takin' off my rubbers
And puttin' my feet on the Northern Lights
As to put 'em on a stove like that."

On Dying

In the dusk he could see other boys
Standing around something in the school yard.
One of them seemed to be pointing.
There was something queer in the air—
Something that made him feel uneasy.

As he crossed the road
He saw a smooth flat track in the dust.
It went up the road as far as he could see.
It turned the other way toward the school grounds.
He followed it to the group of boys.
They all looked very solemn.
"There's where he fell."
One of them pointed to a spot on the turf
Where the hoof marks ended.
The grass was trampled around it.
There the flat track began.

Old man Perkins had been working
With his bay horse, Maggie,
Right on that spot, not three hours before.
The old horse had stopped.
She'd raised her head, groaned,
And fallen over, stone dead.

Slowly the boy followed the track in the dust.
He could just see it now in the dusk.
Perhaps tomorrow he could follow it to the end.
He sat down on the steps of his house.

He tried to picture old Maggie,
Her legs out stiff and straight on the stone boat.
He wondered how the horses, drawing that load,
Felt about a comrade dying.
He wondered how old Maggie looked
Down there where they'd taken her.
He didn't like to think of her down there
In Dead Horse Swamp, alone in the dark.
It didn't sound much like a cemetery.
Dying seemed a queer sort of thing.
Somehow Maggie's dying seemed stranger
Than Grandfather's dying, last year.
It seemed more awful.

It was good to find the lamp lighted in the kitchen
And Mother putting something into the oven.

A Gardener

Pat Clark wasn't afraid of work.
He would lie right down beside it
And go to sleep any time.
He usually managed to get enough gardening
To keep himself in tobacco.
He felt that the public
Owed him the rest of his living.
Early in the summer he would get a job
With some newcomer who just had to have someone
To start the garden.
Sometimes he'd last until the planting was done.
More often he was fired at the first pay-day.

By clever management
He'd stayed with Squire Higgins
Almost a month.
The Squire enjoyed his conversation
And overlooked the weeds.
He said Pat saved him the price
Of a subscription to *Puck*.
At last the Squire's wife
Decided she'd take matters
Into her own hands.
Pat was fired.

He was telling the stage-driver
The next day.
"I don't figger the Squire done right.
He might jest as well akep' me
When it takes so tarnation little
To keep me busy."

A Geometrical Figure

Martin Colton was a good carpenter.
He might have been the village contractor
If he had been more ambitious.
Or perhaps he stayed a day laborer
Because he got more out of life
Without too many responsibilities.
He lived in comfort if not in style
And he had time to fish when he felt the need.
His wife was easygoing
And did her house work
As Martin did his carpentering—
When she felt in the mood for it.

One spring Martin was working in the South Village.
A man from the city had come there
And he hired Martin to help fix up the house
On the old Cummings place.
Martin's willingness to change jobs often
Made him a good man for puttering.
When he got tired of work
He'd engage in conversation with Mr. Peterson—
He was the man from the city.
Martin always made it a point to agree
So he got along very comfortably
With Mr. Peterson's positive manner.
Probably Mr. Peterson would have been somewhat amazed
If he had known some of Martin's opinions.

One Saturday evening Martin was at the store
Buying the week's provisions.

84

He stopped to sit a while on the steps.

"Where you workin', Mart?"

It was Ezra Waller talking.

"I'm workin' fer that city feller

That bought the Cummin's' place."

Ezra asked him what he was doing.

"Wal, I build suthin' one day

And tear it down the next."

He gave more details of his work.

"Wal, what kind of a feller is this city man anyhow?"

Ezra held out a plug and Martin bit off a chew.

He got it limbered up; then he said thoughtfully,

"Wal, I figger he's just an imaginary line

Drawed through a suit o' clothes."

Almost a Total Loss

There had been a story going around
That Amos Tomkins,
Some years back,
Had come pretty close
To being buried alive.
They said he was all laid out
In a new pine box
And came to
Just before the friends gathered
For the service.

He was hoeing corn
In the field north of his house.
He stopped his work
And folded his hands
On the end of his hoe.
"Yes, I reckon I come pretty close
T' bein' planted.
But I fooled 'em.
That pine box that Cy Rawlens made
Cost three dollars and forty cents
Countin' time and lumber."
He cut off a piece of plug.
"It come near bein' a total loss.
After they found I wa'n't goin' t' need it,
I kep' it kickin' 'round
Three or four year.
Finally one o' them Higginses
That lived up the rud, died.

By gol, I sold it t' the widder
Fer jest what it cost me."
He hoed a couple of hills.
Then he chuckled.
"Joke of it is
I ain't got m' pay yit,
And it's runnin' nigh onto four year."

A Chimney

On a winter's morning
You could tell
Just when each family got up
By the curling cloud of wood-smoke
Which rose from the chimneys.
Most of those chimneys
Shell had built.

When-the folks from the city
Built over the Burrit place
They opened the old fireplace.
Then they had Shell build the chimney over.
He was a little shaky
About the fireplace
But they wouldn't let him touch it.

When they tried it out
It smoked, just as Shell thought it might.
They blamed the chimney.
Mrs. Tomkins was complaining
To the storekeeper,
Who had recommended Shell.
She suggested that Shell
Didn't know how to build a chimney.
The storekeeper turned to Jim Slocum,
Who was whittling by the stove.
"Jim, that chimbley Shell built for you last fall
Drawed all right, didn't it?"
Jim took his pipe out of his mouth.

"Draw?
I'll tell ye, Mis' Tomkins,
That chimbley Shell built fer me
Drawed so, I had t' stand outside the kitchen
T' catch the wood
It drawed right out the stove."
He spit into the sawdust box.
"Finally hed t' put screenin'
Over the pipe hole inside.
Draw? Goshamighty!"

A Romanticist

Lin was no ordinary liar.
He belonged to the romantic school
Of fiction talkers.
He used his overwhelming creative instincts
Making ordinary events into things of interest.
He began in his youth
By telling tales of adventures
In which he usually figured as hero.
Later in life a creative memory
Enlarged and enriched his field.

Of course most of the townspeople
Had heard his stories over and over.
Some new bit of gossip, nicely embroidered,
Was his only means of getting a hearing.

When summer visitors began to come in
They made a new audience for Lin.
And he made the most of his chances.

One of his old friends
Had heard Lin telling a very large one
To the woman whose garden he was making.
She had been much impressed by Lin.
That night the friend told Lin
He ought to be ashamed
To deceive that city woman with such talk.
"Lin, I don't believe you could tell the truth
Even if y' tried."

Lin looked surprised and a little hurt.
"Yep. I could do it."
He chewed a straw a minute.
Then, pleased with a new idea he added,
"And I would if I could ever think of it."

Crazy Williams

If you wanted to scare the wits out of a child
All you had to do was to yell:
"Here comes Crazy Williams."
Of course he was harmless,
But his wandering gait and creepy look
Made him fearsome and fascinating.
He'd stop quite often and shake his legs.
He was shaking the devils
From his pant legs.
Sometimes he carried a chain
To flay the devil with.

One afternoon he shuffled up the steps
Of the general store in the village.
As usual he stopped to shake out the devils
Before he went in.
The storekeeper looked up and greeted him.
He finished weighing some sugar
And, lighting his pipe, he sat down near Edgar.

"How does it happen that you have so much trouble
Fighting off the devil, Edgar?
He never bothers me."
Edgar looked at the storekeeper,
His head shaking as it always did.
"He don't never bother
Them that he's sure of," he said.

The Miller

That low weathered building
With the platform under the overhanging roof
Is Silas Wetherbee's grist mill.
There's a big water wheel turning slowly
In the stream which runs from the small pond.
When Silas is grinding the whole building quivers.
You have to shout to make yourself heard.
Silas is a small man
And his hat and clothes are white with meal.

When he goes to meeting Sunday morning
He looks like a different man.
His hair is black and his beard only slightly gray.

Six days a week Silas is always working
Grinding grain, filling bags, loading it onto scales,
And helping farmers put it on their wagons.
At night, before he goes to supper,
He turns off the water and goes to the small office
In one corner of the grinding room.
He posts his books at a high desk
Using a short pencil which he wets often in his mouth.

In one corner on a table there is a cage.
There's a wheel at one end.
In it a gray squirrel runs hour after hour.

At night Silas goes to that house
With white pillars under the piazza.

93

He inherited the house and mill from his father.
His wife is as busy all day as her husband.
She is keeping every speck of dust out of the house.
She makes Silas take off his mill clothes
In the shed before he comes into the kitchen.

They have one son.
He went West when he was twenty-one.
Steady citizens could never understand his going.
He might have stayed right there
And run the mill with his father.
Some day he would own it.

Perhaps he'd watched the gray squirrel
In the cage in the mill office.

An Agricultural Expert

Henry Stubbs was talking.
He was telling the usual group
Around the stove in Sedgwick's store
How to make money on a farm.
He was a farmer himself
And so he spoke with authority.
He showed what mistakes most of the farmers were mak-
  ing.
Many of them, he felt,
Were paying too much attention to dairying.
What every farmer in the valley should do
Was to pay more attention to apples.
"Yessir, the money lies, jest now,
In raisin' apples. I know it.
I'm goin' to trim up the old orchard
And set out a few thousand new trees besides."

He took an envelope from his pocket.
It was covered with figures.
He went into details of spraying costs
And storage and market charges.
He finished with a clear profit
Of not less than five thousand dollars.

He walked over to the counter
Where the storekeeper was marking some goods.
He'd been listening to the lecture.
There was a twinkle in his eye.
"Ef them fellers would just use their heads

A mite more, they'd git somewheres."
He repeated his apple argument.
Then he said, in an off-hand manner,
"Give me a couple o' plugs of Old Tar;
And I want five pounds of brown sugar."
The storekeeper put the goods on the counter.
Henry picked them up slowly.
"Guess you'd better book 'em.
Ma didn't git her egg money this week."

Cash and Credit

The weather-beaten sign over the door
Read "D. Galusha, Dry Goods, Hay and Grain."
Steep steps led to a covered porch
Littered with crates and boxes and barrels.
Inside, showcases on two sides
Were covered with a disorderly array of boxes.
From the ceiling hung pails and lanterns.
On a counter at the back
There were piles of overalls and jumpers
And a few shoddy suits.
Around the stove in the middle of the room
There were chairs and a bench
Made of a board set on two nail kegs.
It was dark in there on the brightest day.
At night three bracket lamps with smoky chimneys
Gave out a faint glow.
Then D. Galusha had a hand lamp
That he used when he needed to go into the back room.

Six days a week he had worked there
For over thirty years.
At night, when the day's business was over,
He would sit on a stool at a high desk
And post his books.
Then he'd take the money out of the drawer
And put it in a bag.
He carried this home and kept it under his bed.
He never knew just how he stood financially.
He never had time to balance his books.

97

He had enough to meet his bills
And that was all he asked of his business.

"That pair o' pants 'll cost you three dollars cash."
He'd look over his glasses at his customer.
Then if he had to put it on the book
He'd make the charge two-fifty.
"You see," he'd say,
"If the feller fergits t' pay his bill
I figger I don't lose so much that way."

The Cobbler

Joel Henderson, the cobbler,
Lives there next to the store.
He lives alone in two rooms
Back of the shop, since his sister died.

His shoulders are bent.
Bushy eyebrows hang over his black eyes.
His hair is long and almost white.
He looks nearer eighty than sixty.

To see him you'd never believe
He used to be the best-dressed young fellow
At the dances in the Town Hall.
He went with every good-looking girl
That lived the length of the valley.
He could have had his pick too.

Then all at once he left the village.
After a while the news got around
That he'd married a woman over in New Hampshire.
He hadn't even told his sister.

Joel was gone several years.
He came back one evening on the train.
His clothes were shabby.
He looked old and tired.
He hardly spoke to George Stone
When he got off the train that night.
He just said he didn't want a ride
And started for the village afoot.

He opened up the old cobbler shop
That had been closed since his father died.
Then he sold the house—the one below the church—
And he and his sister moved into the rooms
Back of the shop.

He never talked.
Even his old friends could get nothing out of him.
Once a woman came to the village.
She had a little girl with her.
They went to see Joel.
They only stayed an hour.

Joel gets more and more crabbed.
The only person he pays any attention to
Is one of the Stebbins' small girls, Ella.
He often smiles at her when he talks.
It's funny too. He never calls her Ella.
He calls her Mary.

The Old Captain

The Captain used to sit
In front of the general store.
They had a special chair for him—
He was too large for chairs that ordinary mortals use.
Six feet seven in his sox.
In his prime he tipped the beam
At something over three hundred.

He used to sit out there and doze in the sun
Until someone, with time to spare, would stop.
Then he'd talk, his long white beard
Shaking up and down to emphasize some point
In politics or war.
The old fires would burn
And his mouth would shut with the snap of youth,
For just a little while.
Then a tired old man would doze,
His white beard heaving as he breathed.

One day a little boy, holding tight to his mother's hand,
Passed by.
He saw the Captain's heroic form,
And the patriarchal beard,
And the massive head crowned with white.
He stood and gazed.
Then, drawing his mother close,
He whispered as one would in church:
"Mother! Is that God?"

Knowing the Captain
I should say that was not sacrilege.
He belonged to that family.

The Atheist

Amos Cadwin was called the town atheist.
He was not orthodox, that was all.
He rather enjoyed the distinction.
It set him apart from the rest
And gave some people the idea that he was a thinker.
Today he would simply be called a liberal.

There had been a revival at the village church
Under the leadership of a visiting exhorter.
This was followed by a series of meetings
Held in the various schoolhouses outside the village.
These were conducted by the deacons.
They were generally experience meetings.
Following long prayers by several of the elders,
People arose and told of the benefits
Their religious experience had brought to them.
Under the stress of emotion they bared their souls.

It was a bitter cold night when Deacon Brill
Stopped at Amos Cadwin's door.
He was on his way to the schoolhouse up the valley,
Where Deacon Clark was to have charge of the meeting.
Deacon Brill asked Amos to go with him,
Feeling, perhaps, that bringing an atheist to the fold
Would add a bright jewel to his crown.
Amos was feeling in a mellow mood that evening.
Then he thought that anything that would bring a man
To drive five miles such a night as that,

Must have some value in it.
So he went.

Deacon made the opening prayer, of some length.
Two others followed.
Then Deacon Brill arose and bowed his head.
He covered the whole history of mankind.
For eleven minutes by the slow-ticking clock on the wall,
He told the Lord the things he should know.

As Deacon Brill and Amos drove home
Amos kept expecting a personal plea, but there was silence.
At last Deacon Brill asked Amos what he thought
Of the prayer of Deacon Clark.
Amos expressed polite approval.
Brill clucked to the horse.
"I didn't think much of it," he said.
"No, sir, Cadwin, I knocked the spots off his prayer
With that one o' mine."

After that Amos always spoke of "Spot Brill."
He was still the town atheist.

Holy Night

As Doctor Stevens came into the village
He let his horse slow down to a walk.
The moon broke through the clouds.
There was not a track on the new-fallen snow.
He was thinking how nice it was
That the Judson baby had come on Christmas eve.
He smiled his pleasant smile
As he passed lighted houses with trimmed trees inside.

What could Ellen Hicks be doing up at this late hour?
She didn't have anyone to be filling stockings for.
Poor thing! She didn't have anything to fill a stocking
    with.
A shadow moved regularly across the drawn shade.
She was sitting there rocking—rocking.

The village clock struck eleven.
From the south came the faint tinkle of sleighbells.

The snow creaked as he went up the steps.
The rocking stopped.
The light moved through the door into the hall.
Ellen unlocked the door.
She held the light up to see who her late caller was.
She had a worn patchwork quilt around her shoulders.

The Doctor went over to the chunk stove to warm his
    hands.
It gave out no heat. He touched it. It was barely warm.

No, of course there wasn't anything the matter with her.
She always sat up until midnight on Christmas eve.
She'd got to thinking about that Stebbins family,
And sat there rocking and forgot her fire.
How they could get along with all those young ones,
And him all crippled, she couldn't see.
They didn't even have wood to keep them warm.

"Ellen, have you been giving wood to the Stebbinses?"
She admitted she had called the boy in and loaded his sled.
Well, maybe she had sent some food.

Little by little the truth came out.
Her nephew did look after her; he always had.
But he'd told her she'd got to stop this sharing.
She'd promised.
But she couldn't bear to think of those Stebbinses.
She could get along. She still had wood in the shed.
The Doctor's scolding stuck in his throat.
He went to the shed and brought in the last armful of
    wood.

He shut the stable door.
He stopped to look down on the sleeping village.
So Ellen had to share.
He recalled the look on her face.
Sharing. That was what Christmas meant.

The clock in the village struck twelve.
Down in the valley a rooster crowed.
Overhead the moon moved slowly across the winter sky.
Holy night. Peaceful Night.

Down the Lane

Through the thick foliage you can see a roof
At the end of that crooked lane.
Some of the village people look down that lane
At the light shining through the leaves
And shake their heads.
And yet a happily married couple lives there.

Maria Beers was angular, dyspeptic and pious.
Which was cause and which effect is no matter.
She ruled her mother and sister Ellen
With a force of will guided by a New England conscience.
She seemed to enjoy the hard things of life.
She could do for those in any kind of trouble,
But she had no understanding of those who rejoiced.
Life was not a thing to be enjoyed; it must be endured.
Rewards would come in heaven.

Ellen was inclined to plumpness.
She had a clear ruddy complexion
And no efforts on the part of Maria
Could hide the fact that her sister was pretty.
This Maria took as an additional burden.
Once Ellen appeared with her hair frizzed.
There was an awful scene, and from then on
Ellen seemed to give up.
With a dogged determination she scrubbed and slaved
Dominated by Maria's stern will.

One evening, when Maria thought she was at meeting,
Ellen met Bill Hingham at the end of the lane.

They must have met there before but nobody knew it.
They drove to a Justice of the Peace in Dorset.
The first news Maria had of the wedding
Was that evening about nine.
She had been wondering what kept Ellen
When she was startled by the ringing of the door-bell.
As she held up the lamp to see who was there
Ellen threw her arms around her husband's neck
And gave him a resounding kiss.
Maria nearly spilled the lamp
But she did have enough strength left
To slam the door.

Now Ellen frizzes her hair when she wants to.
Someone told Maria that she and Bill
Had been seen at a dance down in the Borough.
No wonder some folks shake their heads
When they look at that house
At the end of the crooked lane!

Change

Progress came marching up the long hill.
It marched through the quiet village and went on,
Leaving that long gray track
Which winds in a narrowing ribbon up the valley.

It caught up the life of the village
And carried it to the big towns.
It left the store with empty, staring windows.
It closed the weather-beaten church.
It scattered the people up and down the valley.
Now there is just a row of scattered houses
Along the new highway.
The village has died.

Three old men sit on the store piazza.
The door is locked; the shelves are empty.
The old men remember when, on a Saturday,
There would be a dozen teams hitched in front.

The old men watch the cars whir past.
They follow one and another with their tired eyes.
They seem to be expecting someone who never passes.
One of them leans against a post and dozes.
He opens his eyes when a noisy truck shifts gears.
Then he drifts off to sleep again.

Their gaze always comes back
To that one spot across the road.
There is the world they've lived in.

Over there tall elms droop over matted grass
And vines, twisting among thorny bushes,
Almost hiding the rows of gray, leaning stones.

There the three old men sit.
In the world whirling past on the gray track of progress.
Of the world across there under the drooping elms.

And on the hill three children
Are looking up into the sky,
Where a silver airplane flashes in the sun.

II

BEYOND THE COVERED BRIDGE

The Covered Bridge

The covered bridge used to look like a dark tunnel.
When a team went through at a trot
The clattering roar almost scared you.
You grabbed the fence which guarded the sides.
From there you could look down into the river.
In the spring it had been black and rushing and angry.
Now there were piles of rocks with quiet streams between.
Right down by the abutment there was a deep black hole.

You wandered into the bridge.
How cool it was in there over the water!
The dust on the planks was cool too on your feet.
You pushed it up in a little pile
And then let it sift between your toes.
Part way through there was a short plank.
You could look down, right into that black hole.
When the sun was right, you could see lazy suckers
Lying there with their fins and tails waving slowly.

On the sides by either end, there were posters.
The circus bills stayed until a new show came along.
Then there were the auction bills
And the prancing horse cured by Kendall's Spavin Cure.

Through that bridge Doctor Stevens drove that night.
He didn't obey that HORSES AT A WALK sign.
Neither had Father, when he went after him.
Of course you weren't there to see
But you arrived at your house soon after;
So you were told some time later on.

A few years later you found the bridge a fine place
To rest the horse when you had Her out for a buggy ride.
Many a couple drove in there
And came out the other end into a new world.

Most of the folks up there on the green hillside
Took their last ride over those knotty planks.

The old covered bridge is full of mystery—
The mystery of life's procession.
There's romance in each of its pegged timbers.

The Elm at the Crossroads

Of course a tree is just so much timber
Or so many cords of firewood.
The timber may make a home
Or the firewood may keep it warm.
But a tree like the elm at the crossroads
Has seen too much of life
To be just timber or firewood.

There it is with its thick trunk on the ground.
They're chopping out the branches
And digging around the broad stump.
Count the rings. A hundred and eight.
It could tell you a lot of history.
It was young when Factory Point was beginning.
There was the Tannery along the river
With piles of bark in the yard.
There was the woolen mill with its whirling looms,
And a dozen other mills along the stream.
It really was Factory Point.

Think of all the people who have passed that tree!
Think of the slow-plodding oxen with loads of goods;
Heavy creaking wagons with blocks of marble
From the quarries on Dorset Mountain;
Gay prancing horses drawing shining buggies;
Lines of soldiers going to save the Union;
Processions in somber black;
Gay parades with bands and flying banners;
Ladies walking with parasols held over quaint bonnets;

Men with high hats and tailed coats;
Statesmen, scholars, warriors, artists—
All have passed under its spreading branches.

There it lies. Just so many cords of firewood.
Of course it had to go.
It's a martyr to what we hope is progress.
Our rushing life cannot be stopped by a tree.

A hundred and eight years
To grow some firewood.

A Reason for Spinsters

Miss Stevenson had taught in the village school so long
That none of the school committee which had hired her
Was in the land of the living.
She was one of those rare souls known as a "born teacher."
She had come from the South
And only a few knew anything of her background.
Everybody in the village felt her presence.
Her voice was low and her slight Southern accent
Went well with the softness of the lines of her face.
She was a gentlewoman to her fingertips
Yet there was no weakness in her backbone
As some of her early pupils had found out.
She took part in many of the village activities
Yet people felt they never quite knew her.
There were inner rooms into which they had glimpses
But where only now and then did anyone enter.

Perhaps it was because of what she kept in the inner rooms
That many of her pupils in after years
Came to her with their deepest problems.
If she could not fully solve them
She gave them something which made them go on trying.
She had a delightful sense of fun
And now and then she would give herself up
To unrestrained girlish gaiety.

She'd been in that mood one evening
At a church supper where she was sitting
Next to Dr. Tower, a friend of long standing.

The Doctor had been a widower for over a year
And the sight of the two evidently enjoying themselves
Sent a pleasant hope through the minds of their friends.
Miss Stevenson had been delighted at one of the Doctor's
    stories
And her laughter was subsiding into chuckles.
The Doctor turned to her and said,
In one of his not unusual outbursts of frankness,
"Nellie, I've often wondered how it ever happened
That you've lived all these years an old maid."
This was penetrating pretty close to the closed room.
There was a sudden silence at the table,
But Miss Stevenson, with only a moment's hesitation, said:
"I've remained a spinster from choice, Doctor Tower."
Then with something between a tear and a twinkle she
    added,
"But it wasn't my choice."

The Wrong Paper

The Post Office boxes were at the right
As customers went into Garret's General Store.
They were all call boxes on many of which
The numbers were about worn off.
Henry had bought them of a former Postmaster
Who had served the public for many years
In another store which closed when the owner died.
After a few summer boarders came to the village
Henry Garret started selling a few newspapers,
Mostly Boston Globes and Heralds.
Then a New York Tribune representative
Offered to send Henry a few of his papers each day,
Having arranged with the stage driver from the station
To get them from the baggage car.

Soon after that Henry was looking out of the window
When a car drove up with a strange man in it.
Henry mistrusted he was the man
Who had bought the Kellogg place.
In reply to the stranger's hearty "Good morning"
Henry murmured "do" and kept on looking out.
The stranger hesitated a minute
And then nodded to the group of sitters.
He asked Henry if he had a New York Times.
Henry walked over to the counter
And held out a copy of the Tribune.
"Folks 'round here read this," he said.
The stranger bought it and then asked
If there was any way he could get a Times each day.

Henry didn't know anything about the Times
But he suddenly remembered.
"There's a couple o' old maids livin' down the street.
Newcomers—only ben here four, five years.
They get the New York Times reg'lar through th' mail."
The stranger expressed interest in such a phenomenon.
"Yep," the storekeeper went on,
"They come here from away and bought the old Hull
    house.
Ben raisin' hell with it ever sence.
'Restorin'' it they call it."
With a hint of a twinkle in his eye the stranger said:
"And they read the New York Times, do they?"
Henry straightened out some things on the counter.
"Yep. Hurt 'em some, too. Made folks standoffish
'Til they got t' know 'em better."

When Grandma Went Away

In the east bedroom upstairs
Grandma lay on the high bed.
More than eighty years before
She'd been born in that same room.
There she'd brought her children into the world.
There seven years back her husband had died.
It was a room filled with memories.

As Grandma grew weaker
She lived over and over the old days.
Her lips moved.
Lights and shadows crossed her face—
Her face finely chiseled and white;
As though it came from the marble mountains
Surrounding the valley farm.

The last things had been done for the night.
The old house was still.
Outside, the big elm her father had planted
Creaked in the winter wind.
The daughter, who sat by the wood-stove,
Turned the lamp down.
Grandma moved her thin arm in protest.
Her daughter leaned over the bed.
"You mustn't take the light away,"
Grandma whispered. Her eyes were closed.
"Don't you see? All my old friends are here."

All through the night she smiled her greeting.
She'd whisper a few words.
Then her lips would move with no sound.

As the first light of the cold December dawn
Showed above the dark line of the East Mountain,
All of the old friends slipped quietly away . . .
And Grandma went with them.

The Lighthouse

On dark nights you'll see a light
Up there on the hill back of the village.
That's Captain Judson's lighthouse.

Molly Watson grew up on that farm.
One spring she went to visit some relatives
Who lived down Cape Cod way.
The next the village heard of her
She'd married a sea captain named Judson.

It was some years before they came back.
Then they came back to stay.
Molly's folks were well along in years.
Besides that, Molly had never got used to the sea.
Every time the Captain took his boat out
Molly would sit and fret and stew.
Any suggestion that she step foot on a boat
Sent cold shivers down her back.
She came to hate the sight of the sea.
So the Captain sold his boat and they came back to the
    farm.
It wasn't long before the Captain
Was longing for the smell of the sea.
To keep himself busy he built that tower
On the north end of the farmhouse.
He made it as much like a lighthouse as he could.
He used to spend much of his time up there.
At night when there was a storm
He would hang a lantern in it.

The year after the old folks died
The Captain disappeared—the call of the sea was too much.
He was gone over a year.
Each night Molly hung the lantern in the lighthouse.
The neighbors noticed she was a little queer.

Then the Captain came back.
He'd been home several years when one morning
They found him sitting in his high tower.
The lantern was still burning.

Every stormy night since then
Molly hangs the lantern in the tower.
She has an idea that the Captain has gone to sea.
She thinks it may bring him
Safe to shore again.

A Musician

That house by the brook belongs to James Huggins.
Back of it is a small shop where he makes shoe pegs.
He uses the brook for power and does quite a business.
He'll never get rich but he always sees to it
That he spends a little less than he gets.
Some of the neighbors think he skimps Harriet,
His wife, on her clothes and housekeeping expenses.

They had one son but he left home years ago.
He ran away one spring day and it was some time
Before they heard from him out in Buffalo.
He and his father never got along together.
He took after his mother's family.
They weren't considered practical.
There were musicians and professors in the line.
James had seen to it that any inherited weaknesses
Didn't develop in Harriet.

Willard, the son, was a dreamer.
All his father's efforts to make him settle down
Aroused a feeling of resentment in him.
On the sly, perhaps with his mother's help,
He learned to play a violin.
It was when his father found this out
That the break came.

After he'd gone, and they knew where he was,
His mother took his absence quite cheerfully.
For the first time in years there was calm in the household.

James went on with his working and saving
And never spoke of his son.

One day a paper came to town.
It told about a concert in Buffalo
Where Willard had played in the orchestra.
He had become a professional musician.
That was too much for his father.
He raved and ranted about it.
He was talking to the Tavern keeper.
"His ma cried," he said with disgust,
"But I swore."

Yes, his mother did cry
But not for the reason James swore.
James doesn't know that.
He never will.

Two Dreamers

On the edge of the village there's a small farm.
There is a weather-beaten barn and shed
And a cottage which still shows signs of having been pink.
Rose Cabot chose that color
The last time her brother, Amos, painted the house.
Pink has always been her favorite color.

Amos is reported to have had various love affairs
But he never seemed interested in matrimony.
Rose has been ready to wed ever since she was fifteen,
But no man ever looked at her twice.
Even now, when there are men around, she titters.

Sometimes she hints to strangers
That she cherishes in her maidenly bosom
The memory of a lost lover.
As the years pass he becomes more and more real.
He assumes the characteristics of the hero
Of the last love-story she has read.
Most of these heroes tread the pages
Of a pink-covered monthly: *The Home Library*.
With a sigh, perhaps a tear, she admits she is sentimental.

Her days of glory came that winter
When she joined a group of Spiritualists.
Then the medium called back to her side
The lover she had never had.
What nights of ecstasy in that darkened parlor
Filled with strange rappings and eerie voices!

Evenings, she and Amos sit by the kitchen table.
Amos, his stockinged feet in a chair,
Reads the *Troy Times*.
Then his head falls back
And his beard points toward the ceiling.
Sometimes he dreams of his old loves
And he smiles in his sleep.

Rose reads her pink-covered monthly.
Then she shuts her eyes
And dreams of the lover who never was.

The lamplight is dim.
The clock ticks on its shelf over the sink.
The teakettle on the stove
Sings softly to itself.

Red Hair

They were moving the dust of the family
Collected under a group of tombstones
In the old farm burying-ground.
After resting there for years
A more prosperous generation had erected a mausoleum
In the cemetery.
The two diggers discovered a last stone
Hidden in a thicket of thorn apples.

"Come near missin' this one.
Looks as though it'd been forgot a-purpose.
There . . . What you make out on the stun?
Git the light on it . . . Scrape some o' that moss off.
There . . . there's a figger . . . one eight one six.
Tip it a mite, there . . . 1797.
Young . . . hold on . . . here's a name . . .
M l l . . . Melissy . . . that's it."

While they ate their dinner under the trees
The old man recalled hearing about Melissa.
She had red hair.
There'd been a red head in each generation.
He recalled hearing his mother tell about her.
She disgraced the family somehow.
"Now I recollect . . . She run off with a peddler.
Come back after a couple o' months . . .
Said he was coming for 'er come fall.
Let's see . . . Suthin' happened to 'er.
Anyhow the feller never come.

129

It comes to me now . . . they found her one mornin'—.
Must 'a' b'en in the creek back the house—
Her red hair was ketched in a willow branch.
Like enough that's why they ain't any Scriptur'
Ner verses on the stun. . . ."

The hot sun beat on their backs as they dug.
They cut through a mass of roots.
"Yessir . . . they said her hair was red as fire.
I've heard Ma say, 'Red as Melissy's hair.'
Don't callate we'll find much.
Here's some wood dust . . . and some white . . .
Put it into this box here.
Wal, guess that's all. Hold on—
What in time . . . that ain't just dirt . . .
Red! . . . Lord! . . .
No wonder Ma used to say,
'Red's Melissy's hair.' "

Public Spirit

No matter how fine the day
Or how well things were going with him,
Dell Stillman couldn't walk down the street
Without seeing something that needed fixing.
Often he'd stop to do the job himself.
Things like filling in a hole in the sidewalk
Or breaking off an overhanging branch.
If it happened to be raining hard,
Or when a thaw was loosening up the winter,
It always took Dell a long time
To get down to his store.
There were always plugged ditches
And he took real small-boy delight
In getting the water running freely again.
Of course, he thought it was a sense of public duty
Which made him play in the water.
If anyone was making some improvements
He'd stop and usually suggest improvements in the im-
    provements.
Of course, when any kind of work
Was being done by the town
His duty as a citizen demanded that he be sure it was well
    done.
After passing Mrs. Harrow's broken gate several days
He took it to his store one morning
And not only fixed it but gave it a coat of paint.

One Sunday morning the minister
Had preached an especially stirring sermon.

As the people came out they were telling each other
How moved they had been by the parson's effort.
One was about to say as much to Dell
When Dell took hold of the step railing.
He shook it and said, "Look at this."
He gave it another shake and said:
"First you know somebody's going to get hurt."
Feeling as though he'd been doused with cold water
The man who had been enthused by the sermon
Hesitated a moment while he got down
To the very practical earth where Dell spent his time.
Trying to control his voice he said:
"Dell, I verily believe when St. Peter
Opens the gate for you you'll stop half way in.
You'll turn to St. Peter and you'll say,
'That gate needs a few drops of oil.' "

Saving Grace

When Miles was a young fellow
Of course he had to work.
Folks admired him for sticking to it.
He made a point of never losing any time.
He went from farm to farm, year after year,
Filling in when any help was needed.

He saved every cent he earned
And loaned it on good security.
He never let his money be idle
And he always collected his interest.
By the time he was fifty
He could have retired on a modest income,
But he kept on working and saving.

He began to show his age.
His hair turned white
And his shoulders became bent.
Folks called him an old miser—
Never taking any pleasure with his money.
Day after day he worked.

One Sunday in autumn
He was walking down the mountain.
He was on his way to help a farmer
Down the valley.
He stopped to rest by the watering trough.
A friend drove up and unchecked his horse.
He passed the time of day with Miles.

He noticed that Miles had aged.
"What on earth do you keep on workin' fer?"
He said to Miles.
"Here you slave on till ye die
And leave a lot o' money fer relatives to blow in."

Miles' blue eyes rested on the distant valley.
"Well, sir," he said in his gentle manner,
"If they have half as much fun
Aspendin' of it
As I've had asavin' of it,
I shall be perfectly satisfied."

A Test Pilot

Every minute Sam Bassett could spare
From his farm work,
He spent in the horse barn
Working on something mysterious.
He never told a soul what he was doing—
Not even his wife.
And yet it filled most of his waking hours.
He was bringing to pass a dream of years—
He was going to fly.
To his neighbors
He was a quiet plodding farmer.
Only his eyes gave any hint
That he might be a dreamer.

The great day had come.
The secret was out.
Sam Bassett was going to try to fly.
He had carefully carried the wings
From the horse barn
To the roof of the hay barn.
A crowd had gathered, laughing, incredulous.
The old fool wouldn't really try it!

His hands shook as he adjusted the straps.
The crowd grew still
As he stepped to the edge of the roof.
He was really going to try it!

They lifted him up
From the mud of the barn yard.

He wasn't much hurt; just stunned.
They helped him into the house.
"I didn't figger suthin' jest right,"
He told his wife.
"Mebbe I'm too old,
But some day they'll be flyin'."

That night at supper tables
They joked about Sam and his flying machine.
"Crazy fool," somebody said,
Sitting by the comfortable fire
In the village store.
The storekeeper put a fresh chunk in the stove.
"Wal, I dunno.
Most of us ain't got the grit
Even t' git up as high as a barn roof."

A Health Note

Ezra Perrin's family, on his mother's side,
Had all been short-lived.
Ezra had been a spindling boy.
He had grown into a man with a constitution
Which could have stood several amendments.
He married when he was twenty-one.
Fortunately his wife was strong
And used to hard work.
With a little help from Ezra,
When he wasn't having one of his bad spells,
She managed to get a living for the family.
Their two children took after their mother.

Ezra used to putter around the wood pile
And, working a little at a time,
He'd get up enough for the winter.
In summer he did a little in the garden.
He spent much of his time in a rocker
On the front porch, when it was warm enough.
In winter he hugged the kitchen stove.
When he went to the village
He wore a faded tippet wound several times
Around his long thin neck.
His visored cap was pulled over his ears.
His long black coat flapped in the wind.
Even in summer he wore the same cap.
He was never quite warm.

He was sitting in the rocker
One spring day.

He'd just finished piling the wood in the shed.
A neighbor stopped his team in the dooryard.
"Well, Ezry, how you feelin' today?"
Ezra stopped rocking.
"Pretty good," he said in a throaty, tired voice.
"I been ailin' so much, I kinder got so's
I feel better when I'm sick
Than I do when I'm well."

Scat

If you'd heard Jehiel talking at the store,
Or when he was getting his corn ground,
Shouting above the roar of the mill,
You would have gained the impression
That he was a man who would rule.
His neighbors had learned
That it was simply the bursting forth
Of what he had to keep bottled up at home.
Among his women folks he was as meek as Moses.
Probably his loud talk
And domineering manner, away from home,
Was his method of keeping his self-respect.

Of course he was the swaggering male
When he was with his cattle and his dogs.
When it came to the cats of the family
He was again more careful.
When they were not in too great favor
He would sometimes show the women
Who was running things,
By chasing all the cats out of the house.
He felt this action must raise him
In the estimation of the household.

A summer visitor had wandered up the road.
He stopped in front of Jehiel's house.
He was looking at the row of four cat-holes
Cut in the bottom of the kitchen door.
Just then Jehiel came out.

As soon as he saw the stranger,
His meek house-broken manner
Gave place to his most manly one.
The stranger spoke of the cat-holes
And suggested that it would seem that one would do.

Jehiel threw out his chest.
"No, sir, one would not do."
He pointed his finger at the door.
"I have those four holes because we house four cats."
"But couldn't they go out one hole in turn?"
The visitor asked.
Jehiel raised his voice.
"No, sir, they could not.
When I holler scat
I mean SCAT."

Hard Cider

Every fall Gard gathered the apples,
Most of which had fallen to the ground,
And took them to the cider mill.
In his father's day
It had been a good orchard.
He had kept the trees trimmed
And only a few windfalls
Went to the cider mill.
He made cider vinegar and sold it.

Gard had let the orchard go
As he had the rest of the farm.
The trees were masses of brush.
The fruit was knotty and small.
He never bothered to pick the apples
Except from one Greening tree
Which still produced fairly good fruit.
When the cider mill had begun to run
Gard would go out with a long pole
And knock off whatever fruit
Was not already on the ground.
Sometimes he had to dicker with a neighbor
For a few more apples.
He had to have enough
To make his winter's supply of cider.

He had worn the cellar stairs thin
Tramping down to fill his pitcher.
He always kept a two-quart dipper by the barrels

And he frequently stopped his work
To go down for a dipperful.

One morning he failed to come for his mail.
Someone was wondering about his absence
When one of his neighbors came in.
"Gard's sick," he said.
"They say he's got a swellin' on his side."
There was a sympathetic silence.
Then one of the sitters emptied his pipe.
"Wal, I don't figger they's any need t'worry.
Like enough he's jest swallered the bung."

A Connoisseur

Hen Loveland had been married three times.
His ventures in matrimony
Had covered a period of some thirty-five years.
His first wife had been only sixteen
When he, a youth of twenty years,
Took her to the Methodist parsonage.
Her parents had plenty of children left.
It was a relief to have one taken off their hands.

It was several years after her death
That Hen began going with the new school teacher.
She was teaching in the North District.
She was somewhat older than Hen
And she felt sorry for him in his loneliness.
They were married in his parlor
The day after her school closed in June.
He looked quite spruced up.
The neighbors had never seen him look so neat.

It wasn't long before the school teacher found
That her savings-bank account was of more interest to Hen
Than any charms she might possess.
In less than a year she left him.

He was sitting on his dilapidated front porch.
His third wife was moving around back of the house.
She brought in wood from the small pile.
As soon as smoke began to come out of the chimney

She came out with a milk pail on her arm.
She went to the pasture bars calling: "C'boss, c'boss."

"Yes," Hen drawled. "She makes out to be
An all-fired good woman.
She's got a crooked spine and mebbe she lacks
Suthin' when it comes to her head."
He whittled a stick for a minute.
"Be that as it may, she's a fair cook,
She kin milk a cow, weed a gardin, chop wood,
And I hev knowed her t' take a hand at plowin'."
He closed his knife and put it in his pocket.
"Book larnin' may be all right 'n its place,
But when it come t' gittin' a wife
I' ruther hev 'em a little mite simple."

A Family Orchestra

Perhaps you'd better wait for a moonlight night
To visit Ike Allenby's place, outside the village.
Then you will miss the shabbiness of it.
In the moonlight its vine-covered walls have beauty.
Lamplight shows through small windows.
Perhaps you'll hear Ike's fiddle.

All of Ike's children play some instrument.
They often play for dances.
What they get helps out considerably,
The living they manage to get from their small farm.
With the kind of care it gets it's a wonder
The farm grows anything but weeds.

Ike's mother was French.
She cooked in the camp
Where his father worked as a lumberjack.
Probably it is the French blood
Which makes Ike something more than a fiddler.
His violin means something to him
Which his hard-working neighbors cannot understand.
To them the family is just plain shiftless.

One fine hay day the neighbors heard Ike and the boys
Playing tunes in the parlor.
They had a lot of hay down too.
In the hayfield they had disagreed
About a new piece they'd been trying the night before.
Ike knew it went like this; he hummed it.

One of the boys knew it went down there
With a little run at the end of the measure.
To settle it, they tied the horses to the fence
And adjourned to the cool parlor.
They tuned their instruments and began to play.
Of course they forgot the haying.

The Parson said to Ike one day:
"I verily believe, like Nero of old,
You'd fiddle while Rome burned."
"Well, Parson," said Ike, tightening his E string,
"I don't know of any better way
Of fergittin' trouble."

Blind Beers

For years the dancing feet of the valley
Had stepped to the music of Blind Beers' fiddle.
When he was seen walking down the road
With his well-worn cane tapping in front of him,
And his fiddle case strapped to his back,
Everyone knew there would be dancing that night.

As soon as the supper dishes were done
The kitchen floor was cleared.
When the weather was warm enough
Even the kitchen stove,
With a piece of wood still smoking inside,
Might find itself standing on the back porch.
Horses were hitched to convenient trees in the yard.
Probably, in the downstairs bedroom,
Several babies slept peacefully on the high bed,
While their parents whirled merrily in the kitchen.
There the perspiring dancers "balanced corners"
And. "docedoed" and "sashayed all."
Blind Beers chanted the calls
As he sawed on his fiddle.

In the midst of a dance in the Borough
The fiddling stopped suddenly.
The E string had snapped.
With solemn face Blind Beers called for a light.
It was his favorite joke.
Willing hands brought candles.
They held them near so Blind Beers could fix the string.

Then he raised his sightless eyes toward the light bearers
And, chuckling, he told them what a help they'd been.
As they moved away, a little sheepishly, the old man said,
Half apologizing for playing a joke on them:
"The blind tryin' to lead the blind, kinder, wa'n't it?"

Waitin'

Probably if Horace Lodge had been brought up
As the other boys in the village were,
He would have amounted to something.
Because he was the only child
And because he had more money than anyone else,
Horace was completely spoiled.

He went away to a private school.
After several extra terms there,
With the help of a tutor during the summer,
He finally got into college.
He came home about the middle of freshman year.
His mother gave numerous explanations
As to the causes of his return.
Zadok, his father, kept his own council.
He had given his son up some time before.

Horace tried several things after his return.
His mother coaxed his father until he agreed
To buy the grist mill for Horace.
Horace showed considerable zeal in fixing the office.
He had some letterheads printed
And a nice sign put up over the door.
Then his interest waned.
He tried several other things
Including matrimony, but they never lasted.

He knew his folks had money enough
So he didn't need to work.

He became a man of leisure.
Now and then he complained of the old man's stinginess,
And told what he'd do when he came into the family
    fortune.

Zadok was talking to an old friend
He hadn't seen for years.
The friend inquired about the family.
As he was about to go, he asked Zadok
More about his son. He had one the same age.
"What's your boy doing, Zadok?"
Zadok's eyes sought the ground.
He flicked the ash from his cigar and said quietly:
"He's waitin.' "

Not Noteworthy

Judging by the looks of Hen Gilman's yard,
He was a dealer in junk.
The evolution of the wagon could be traced
By the wrecks, partly covered with weeds and brush,
Which filled most of his pasture.
A few broken-down automobiles
Were scattered nearer to the road.
They were more recent acquisitions.

Hen was always trading.
Each time he managed to get a little cash.
The cars represented the last of a series of trades
When no further cash could be involved.

One morning Hen appeared on the road with a truck.
It would run at times,
But Hen seemed to spend much of his time
With his head under the hood.
"Considerin' what I give fer it
I reckon that ain't a bad car."
That was his usual statement
When the situation seemed to demand an explanation.
Such occasions were not infrequent,
So that the curiosity of several of the men
As to what he *had* given, became aroused.

He had stopped in front of the blacksmith's shop.
He was getting a spring fixed.
As usual he was telling what a good truck it was

"Considerin' what I give fer it."

Thurber stopped pumping the bellows.

"Well, what in tarnation DID you give fer that wreck?"

Hen looked surprised.

Then he said, a little apologetically:

"Why, I give m' note."

Looking at a Gift Horse

Marcus was criticizing his Congressman.
He felt his vote had given him that privilege.
He didn't like the seeds he'd sent.
He'd voted wrong on several questions.
In fact the whole bunch of legislators
Came far short of his ideas of statesmen.
At last the real cause of complaint came out.
"They ain't one that's got as much sense as my yearlin'.
There they sit ajawin' and wastin' taxes.
I'd like t' see some real men put into office.
Mebbe then they'd do suthin'
About reducin' this damned dog tax."

Marcus scraped together a living on his farm.
His cattle were walking skeletons.
He refused to pay the robber grain dealers
The prices they asked.
His wife looked half-starved,
And Marcus himself would rather go hungry
Than pay the storekeeper such awful prices.
Now and then he bought something from a catalogue
    house.
He wore the same suit of clothes
When he went to the village
That he'd bought by mail when he got married.

One summer, in the midst of haying, one of his team died.
He was always losing horses.
He refused to grain them and worked them hard.

153

One of his neighbors had loaned him an old horse
To finish his haying with.
Marcus had been using him two weeks
And was about through with the hay crop.
The neighbor stopped one day and asked Marcus
How he was making out with the old horse he'd loaned
    him.
Marcus chewed on a piece of grass.
"Wal, I made out with him."
He threw the grass away and sighed.
"Seems as though he et considerable more
Than my mare does though."

A Joy Ride

Sorrow was the only emotion
Which John Cox ever displayed.
In passing through this vale of tears
No happiness nor joy became a man of real religion.
Things of beauty were snares for unwary feet.
Hannah, his wife, wore only black.
He even forbade a flower bed in the yard.
One year Hannah did have a flower to look at.
The men were cutting the hay in the meadow
South of the house.
There was a tall thistle by the fence
Which Hannah could see from the sitting-room window.
She got the men to save it.
Then she'd sit sewing in her south window
And get all the joy of sinning
Out of looking at the purple thistle flower.

John announced, one day,
That he had to go on business to a neighboring town.
Her people lived a few miles beyond
And he suggested that they'd go there to spend the night.
He frowned at her ill-suppressed elation.
She had not been allowed to see much of her family
For John felt they were a godless lot.
So she prepared for the great event quietly.
When John was out of the house
She went around humming hymn-tunes.
Now and then he rebuked her for unseemly cheerfulness.

They had arrived at the neighboring town at noon.
They ate the cold lunch she had put up,
Sitting in the carriage in the horse shed.
Then John went out to transact his business.
Hannah could hardly contain herself.
She went over the little things she'd secretly brought
As gifts for the home folks:
Some sweet pickles and two jars of jelly.
The time dragged interminably.

At last John came back.
He put the horse back in the thills
And they started down the village street.
Coming to the road running up and down the valley
Hannah saw John turn north again toward home.
She clutched his arm.
"But, John, you've turned the wrong way."
John's mouth was set and he slapped the reins on the horse.
"Yes. We're going back home now.
You've felt joyous long enough already."

Meeting at the Lord's Barn

Eben had spent his Sunday afternoon
Up on the Southeast Corner.
He'd gone up to salt the sheep
In the mountain pasture.
It grew dark as he walked down the mountain.
Lights showed over in the Borough
And on the hills beyond.
As he came to the main road
He heard singing.
It came from Meeting House Hill.
Then Eben remembered there was a revival there
In the half-finished building
Known among the sinners as "The Lord's Barn."

Eben wasn't orthodox in his beliefs.
He didn't like emotional displays.
He probably felt he was wholly irreligious.
Yet he found something soul-satisfying
When he was alone up on the mountain pasture.
It was nothing he could talk about.
He couldn't make it fit a dogma.
He couldn't limit or define it.
It was something the hills distilled.

Eben strolled up to the open door of the Meeting House.
He slipped in quietly
And stood, leaning against the back wall.
The preacher was walking back and forth
In front of the congregation.

He was telling why some folks came to church.
Some came to show their best clothes.
Others came to gossip after the service.
Some came just out of curiosity—
He whirled suddenly
And pointed a bony finger straight at Eben.
"And some come to pick," he shouted.
Then in a deep and damning tone he repeated:
"And some come to PICK."
And Eben turned and picked his way out.

An Uphill Courtship

James Bowers was paying attention to Sally Higgins.
Her folks lived in the last house
On the road that went over to southeast corner.
James was a serious-minded young man
And there was no doubt that he intended to marry Sally
If she'd have him.

One evening in the fall
James got the chores done early.
After supper he put on his best clothes
And harnessed Bess to the new buggy
That he'd bought that summer.
As usual he stopped in at Brayley's store.
He liked to hear the men crack jokes
About his courting Sally,
Though he never said much in reply.

On this night some of the usual crowd
Slipped out soon after James came in.

It was dark when he started up the steep road.
He always settled down in the buggy seat
So his head almost rested on the back.
He noticed for the first time
That going up this road he had to sit up
Or be in danger of going over backwards.
He'd never realized before
How the road seemed to go straight up.

As he drove into the yard, Sally opened the door.
James unfolded his long legs and stepped out.
As Sally came out to meet him
The light shone from the doorway
On the glistening new buggy.
"I'll declare, Sally, it does seem 's though
That hill got steeper every time I come up it."
As he turned to get the tie rope
He suddenly discovered why the boys
Had left Brayley's store just after he had come in.
They'd put the smaller front wheels
On the back axles and the higher back ones
On the front.
Yes, the hill did seem steeper that night
But it was worth climbing,
When Sally put back her head
And laughed.

Botheration

Jacob Hart was a trader.
He'd begun when he was a small boy.
He always had odd things in his pockets
That he was willing to part with
Providing another boy had something
Jacob felt was worth more.
He might get stuck now and then,
But in the long run
He came out ahead.

His farm was a curiosity shop.
He attended all the auctions
And he always brought home a wagonload.
He sold the stuff for cash
Or traded with some cash to boot.
He swapped horses and cattle too.
He had a drawer full of chattel mortgages.

He had traded a yoke of oxen
With Hen Sibley for a cow and some hogs,
With some cash to boot.
Three days later, Hen walked into Jacob's yard.
He evidently had something on his mind.
In plain language he expressed his opinion
Of the oxen Jacob had stuck him with.
He couldn't keep them in the pasture;
They'd broken loose in the barn;
When he managed to get them yoked up
They'd run away.

"You lied t' me, that's what you done."
Jacob shook his head.
"Nope. I didn't tell you a thing that wa'n't so."
Hen knew he had.
He remembered the very words
Jacob had used when he asked about
Whether the cattle were steady and reliable.
"You said they never bothered you a mite."
Hen shook his finger at Jacob.
"Them's the very words you used."
"Well, Hen, they done the same way with me.
But jest as I told you before,
Ye see I don't let nothin' like that
Bother me."

Zephaniah's Repentance

The Emerson Farm was on the hill
East of the village.
If it looks rocky now
You should have seen it
Before Zephaniah Emerson began to work it.
He built those walls you can see from the village
Marking off the pastures and meadow.
Then he dug holes and sank no end of bowlders.
Whenever farmwork was slack
Zephaniah was always getting rid of stones.

Naturally he was saving.
That was how he left a fine farm
And money in the bank for his son.
Of course some of his shiftless neighbors
Thought he was tight and stingy.

He was regular in his going to meeting
But he wasn't always as strict
As some of his neighbors thought he should be.
That was what caused the trouble
When he sold that yoke of oxen.
They were getting old and stiff
And Zephaniah had been trying to sell them
For several months.
One Sunday morning two men came into the yard
And after considerable dickering
They drove off with the oxen.
Before the next Sunday the Board of Deacons

Waited on Zephaniah.
They labored with him on the wickedness
Of selling cattle on the Sabbath.
By the next Sunday they had accomplished nothing.
At last they gave up all hope
Of making him cancel the sale.
All they asked of him was to say he was sorry
He'd sold the cattle on the Sabbath.
Just before meeting the next week
They met him again, with the Minister.
As the bell was tolling for service,
Zephaniah rose and said, hesitating between words:
"Wal, I will say I'm sorry it was Sunday
When I sold them cattle."

The New Road

Ebenezer Fish was certainly "sot."
He was sure that what had been good enough
For his father and grandfather
Was good enough for him.
He ran his farm that way.
He cut his hay by hand
And fed his stock just as they used to.
The fact that some of his neighbors
Got more milk by selecting their cattle
And feeding them by modern rules
Made no difference to him.

Every year at Town Meeting
He could be relied on to object
To most of the taxes.
He especially objected to increased expenses
For schools and educational frills.
He'd learned enough when teachers
Got three dollars a week
And boarded around.

Naturally when they voted to build a new road,
Around the hill between his farm and the village,
He fought to keep the old one
Which climbed laboriously over the crest.
The road had been finished for seven years
But he still continued to use the hill road
To the day he took his last trip
To the village.

He argued just as earnestly about it
As though the new road was just in prospect.
He'd always end his tirade with
His clinching argument:
"No, sir," he'd say,
"That new rud's jest a waste of the town's money.
Ain't it jest as fur around the bale of a pail
When it's layin' down
As 'tis when it's a-settin' up?"

No Humor

Charlie made his living, in winter,
By the use of his saw and saw-horse.
Everybody in the village
Had a neat pile of four-foot wood
Piled in the yard.
It was a matter of family pride
To have a good supply of dry wood
In the shed by spring.
Charlie went around sawing and splitting.
The piling was usually attended to by the family.

Charlie was a good man at the saw.
He got a dollar a cord.
When the big house on the hill
Was built by a man from the city,
The owner sent word to Charlie
That he would like to have him come up.
He had some wood he wanted cut
In two-foot lengths for his fireplaces.
This was not the size which was usual
In the village where stoves were in vogue.
Charlie had sent word that he couldn't come.

The next day he was sawing the Postmaster's pile
When the city man came into the yard.
He hoped Charlie could come up the next day.
Charlie seemed doubtful.
"I'll give you a dollar fifty a cord."
Charlie still hesitated.

The price was raised to one seventy-five.
"Nope," Charlie said with finality,
"I dunno when I can come."

Cyrus Waller had been standing by.
When the city man had gone he said to Charlie:
"Say, you dumbed fool, he offered ye one seventy-five
And cut once at that 'stead of three times.
What in time you thinkin' of?"
Charlie leaned his saw against the horse
And wiped his face with his blue handkerchief.
"Wal, I jest wa'n't a-goin' to humor 'im,
That's all."

A Water Cure

Giles Barton was used to having his own way.
On his farm and in his house
His word was law.
He was tall and broad-shouldered
And he'd never been sick a day in his life.
That made it much harder for him
When, one spring, he came down with the measles.
At first he paid no attention.
He kept right on working.
The second morning he came in from the barn
And threw himself on the sofa in the sitting room.
His face was flushed and his head ached.

He fought against having the Doctor
But that afternoon his wife sent for him.
He looked very grave when he saw Giles.
The rash had not come out
And fever was raging in Giles's big body.
All night he called for water
But any liquid was forbidden in those days.

When the Doctor came the next afternoon
He told Giles his case was serious.
He advised him to make any business arrangements
That were necessary, in case he didn't get well.
Unless the rash appeared soon
The fever would burn him up.

After the Doctor had gone, Giles motioned to his wife.
He told her to go out to the spring back of the house

And bring him a pail full of water.
She argued and pled, but he demanded water.
He was going to die anyway
And he wanted some of that spring water once more.
Finally she gave in.

He seized the dipper from her with feverish strength.
He drank, rested, and drank again.
Then he slept.

The next morning he was covered with rash
Brought out by the water.
The fever was almost gone.

"You see," he said after he was out again,
"When he told me I prob'ly wa'n't goin' to pull through,
I figgered I'd die of suthin' besides thirst.
Besides I wa'n't quite sure 'bout the water supply
Where I might be goin'."

School District Meeting

There had been as many as sixteen children
At the school in district number nine.
They came from six families,
Two of which saw to it
That they always had a good teacher.
Of course the teacher boarded around
And this district had no trouble
In getting a good one.
The teachers knew they would be in good homes.
For some years one of the Bascom girls
Had taught there.
She was a friend of George Ellsworth's wife
And George had been head of the school committee
For ten years at least.

As time went on the children from those families
Who had a real interest in keeping the school up,
Finished their schooling.
At last the only scholars for the next term
Were the four Turnbell children
And Hiram Sexton's six-year-old boy.
Neither one of these parents had ever taken the trouble
To go to any of the school district meetings.
Their connection with the school
Had consisted largely in offering criticisms
Of the teacher and grumbling about the tax.

The district meeting had been held.
A week or so later Jake met George Ellsworth.

"Wal, I s'pose you loaded that same old tax
Onto our shoulders, at the school meetin'."
George wound the reins around the whip.
"Nope. School won't cost you a cent from now on.
We voted to give up havin' school."
Jake took his foot off the hub.
"What in tunkit you mean? No school?"
George smiled.
"You see, Jake, the three of them that were there
Didn't have a young one t' send.
They'd all finished their schoolin'.
As long as there wa'n't anybody there
That had any need fer a school
We decided t' give it up."

Jake and Hiram attended the special meeting
George Ellsworth called a month later.

Hog Culture

Ezra Simpson had tried various ways
Of making a living.
Perhaps it is too much
To say that he tried.
Somehow he managed to get along
With a roof over his head
And food enough to sustain what life he had.
He was very prone to put success ahead of him.
He was always telling what he "callated" to do.

Cynthia married Ezra a year after Will died.
Will was her first husband.
He left her that small farm below the bridge.
It was in fine shape when Will died,
But it was badly run down
When Cynthia decided she needed a man to manage it.
Ezra had been hanging around and helping a little
When, one day, he offered himself
As a successor to Will.
Cynthia, worn out and discouraged, accepted.
Folks said she should have known better.

After trying various agricultural experiments
With his wife's farm,
Ezra finally settled on hog raising
As the most likely line.
He was discussing the business with a group
In the blacksmith's shop.
"Yes, I figger hog raisin'

Is about the best bet jest now."
He whittled away on a piece of soft wood.
"Y' see hogs mostly raise theirselves,
And Cynthy kin fetch th' swill."

The Eden Musee

Mrs. Demming was sitting
On the front porch of the farmhouse.
She was shelling peas while Melissa, a neighbor,
Rocked and talked.
Mrs. Demming had been away.
She had spent three days in New York.
There had been an excursion.
Melissa had come over
To hear all about the trip.
As usual she had been so full of her own news
That she'd learned little
About the sights of the big city.
As soon as Mrs. Demming mentioned
Some point of interest,
It would remind Melissa of something
That happened on her trip to the Centennial.
She and Sylvanus had gone there
On their wedding trip.

At last Mrs. Demming got a chance
To tell about her visit to the Eden Musee.
(Her pronunciation had nothing to do with French.)
She described all of the wonders
Filling the floors above ground.
Then she gave a shuddering recital
Of the bloody scenes in the "Chamber of Horrors."
Sitting on the edge of her chair,
Melissa listened in unwonted silence.
Then she drew a deep breath

And asked in an awe-struck voice:
"My lands, how'd you ever git through sech a place?"
Mrs. Demming stopped shelling peas for a minute.
"Wal, I couldn't never have stood it
'Cept I kep' asayin' over and over t' m'self:
' 'Tain't nothin', 'tain't nothin'.' "
She snapped a pod open and rolled the peas out.
"Now I've got home
I've come to the conclusion
It wa'n't, neither."

Grandma Westcott

All of the Westcotts had been Tories.
Next to her ancestry
Grandma Westcott gloried most in The Church.
The Book of Common Prayer was as much a part of her
As her stiff spine—
A spine which never touched the back of a chair.

The Methodists were having a revival at the Borough.
And there seemed to be "an awakening."
The little church was filled each night
And the visiting evangelist spoke "with power."
Urged on by her neighbors
Grandma, one night, consented to go.
She wished she hadn't before she started.
What could these upstarts know about religion?

She sat bolt upright through the prayers
And never took her eyes off the speaker
As he warmed to his theme.
A good brother booming "A-men" right behind her
Failed to distract her rigid attention.
The evangelist left the pulpit.
He came down the aisle
Urging this one and that
To go forward to the mourners' bench.
He came toward Grandma.
She gazed fixedly at him as he drew near.
Stopping by her seat he said in a sepulchral tone:

"Sister, are you a Christian?"
She gave herself a twist
And sat up straighter than ever.
"Not in this church I ain't."

Fitting the Shoe

If Maria Sellers hadn't lived alone
Perhaps she would not have become the town gossip.
Her mind was active and alert
But it was always busy on things
That didn't amount to anything.
She got most of her information from "They."
"They say" was the usual introduction
To any of her conversation.
Usually her gossip was harmless.
Sometimes it started something which stirred the village.
Then she was the first one to deplore it.

She had clever methods of finding out too.
She might spend a half hour talking in general.
Then she'd suddenly ask you
If you'd heard what "they were sayin'."
It might be something about your best friend.
If you acted displeased
She'd say of course there was nothing in it.
Somehow she'd get more information—
Usually something you didn't mean to let out.
People who thought of her as a comic weekly
Found she was an addition to the village life.
To the ones who took her news as gospel truth
She was a thorn in the flesh.

The sermon had been from the text:
"The tongue is an unruly member."
Gossip had been the subject.

179

All through it Maria had nodded her approval.
After a particularly telling thrust
She looked across to express her approval to a neighbor.

The benediction had no sooner been said
Than Maria reached over and touched the woman in front.
Holding her hand to her mouth,
So as not to be overheard, she whispered:
"My lands! I do wish Elly Sutor had 'a' been here
T' hear that discourse."
She turned away with a virtuous nod.

Prepared

No one knew just how it had happened.
Some said the breeching broke
Letting the load onto the team.
Or Zenas might have slipped,
And fallen between the horses and the sleds—
He always stood up on the logs
Until he got down through the pasture.
He could tell, if he pulled through.
Dr. Moseley said he might lose his left leg anyway.
The Doctor had come back from the hospital
On the evening train.
He'd gone right up to the farm;
Millie, Zenas' wife, was pretty well done up.
They said his mother was going on
Just as though nothing had happened.
One of the neighbors was doing the chores.

The next morning the snow was beginning to melt
In the road that ran up to Zenas' house.
Smoke drifted from the kitchen chimney
And faded into the blue of the February sky.
The load of logs, with one of the sleds smashed,
Lay in the small ravine by the brook.
There were streaks of pink in the trampled snow.

It was too early for spring house cleaning
But the front porch was filled with furniture.
The parlor door was open.
Zenas' mother was shaking a small rug, making it snap.

Millie came out and began to dust a horsehair sofa.
She walked listlessly; her eyes were red.
Zenas' mother bustled in and out.
She could hardly stop to hear any words of sympathy.
Of course the morning's news of Zenas was good
But you could never tell.
They had to have that parlor cleaned
Just in case—
She could not bear to have folks see it the way it was.

   .   .   .   .

Crisp twilight had settled on the valley.
Millie came out on the porch.
She was waiting for the biscuits to brown.
The East Mountains were black shadows.
One brilliant star showed above them.
She'd bake some of those biscuits for Zenas
The night they brought him home.
He always liked them for supper.

In the parlor Zenas' mother was moving the furniture.
She was putting the horsehair sofa back into the corner
Where she'd left a cleared space.

Worked Out

All summer Alfred had worked hard.
His cellar was filled with fruits thereof.
There were forty bushels of potatoes.
There were barrels of apples
And two good-sized casks of apple-juice.
Late in the fall he filled two barrels with pork.
In the butt'ry he had plenty of flour
And corn meal and canned goods.
He also had considerable cash in a tin box
Which he kept in a secret place behind the chimney.

Except for getting in a little wood
And feeding his chickens and milking the cow
He intended to rest for some time.
He turned down several lumbering jobs.
He was always a good hand at chopping.

Along in January he came down with a cold.
His brother who lived next door,
Referred to it as "this here dog distemper."
Suddenly Alfred became worse
And the brother went for the Doctor.
He felt Alfred's pulse and thumped his chest.
He gave him some salts and left some pills
Which Alfred was to take at bedtime.

As the Doctor was putting on his coat
He said to Alfred:
"You just lie quiet and take that medicine

And I'll have you at work
Inside of a week."

Alfred raised himself on his elbow.
"Hold on, Doc," he said in a strong voice,
"You can take them damned little pills with ye.
I don't callate to go to work afore spring
And I ain't sure I'll work then."

Pa is Hindered

The hired man came in from the barn.
He hung his hat by the door
And went over to the sink to wash.
He moved toward the table.
He didn't look up when Ma said:
"Ain't Pa comin' to breakfast?"
He gulped a mouthful of food before he said:
"No. He ain't a-comin' now. He's hendered."
He had a second helping of fried potato.
He drank some coffee and then sat holding the cup.
He kept looking out of the window toward the barn.

"What's keepin' Pa?" she said, filling his cup again.
"Today's the day he had to go to the village.
He had to see suthin' 'bout that note."
The hired man dipped his doughnut in his coffee.
"Thing's wan't jest right 't the barn," he said.
Ma looked up quickly from the stove.
"So Pa's hendered," he added.

He got up slowly and took some time
Picking up his plate and the coffee cup
And shoving the chair up to the table.
He put the dishes in the dish pan.
He went to the cellar-way and got a dipper of water.
"Why on earth don't Pa come?"
The hired man took his hat from the hook.
"Things ain't jest right 't the barn."
He looked out of the door.

He twisted his hat in his hands.
He put it on his head.
He started to go out.
He turned and took his hat off.
Almost in a whisper he said:
"Pa's hung hisself."

The Day of Rest

Sunday on the Hood place
Was always a cloudy day.
Except for the absolutely necessary chores,
Nothing in the way of work was allowed.
Any kind of play was out of the question.
The two girls accepted the parental edict,
Attending church with due decorum,
And spending the long afternoon
In proper reading.

Elisha, the only boy, began to rebel early,
And caused his parents much concern.

On a beautiful crisp autumn Sabbath
His mother was unspeakably shocked
To find him busy with hammer and saw
Back of the barn.
He was making a box-trap for skunks.

His father usually attended to stern disciplinary measures
But he was having his Sunday nap
Following a heavy dinner.
So Mrs. Hood approached Elisha,
And, in a voice trembling with horror and rage, said:
"Lige Hood. Stop that this minute!
Don't you know this is the Sabbath—
The day of rest?"
Lige threw his saw on the ground.
"Ma, how in hell can a feller rest
When he ain't tired?"

Gabriel

In the old days, in the Borough,
Most of the men had nicknames.
They were usually given
Because of some physical or mental peculiarity
Or because of some family trait.
Many of the nicknames went so far back
That the oldest inhabitant
Couldn't tell where they came from.

Caleb Smith had a nickname
Which anyone could understand.
For years and years he dug the graves
In the cemetery on top of the hill.
In the early days some member of the family
Performed this last service,
Or a neighbor would offer to do it
As a mark of respect and a token of sympathy.

As time went on
Caleb Smith became the regular grave-digger.
From then on he was always known
As "Gabriel" Smith.

He played in the Sunderland Band
But he didn't play a trumpet.
He played the bass drum.

Store Teeth

In those days
A person had good teeth
Or he didn't have any.
Removal was the only cure
For defective molars.
A few people who could afford it
Proudly displayed perfect sets
Of pure white unnaturally regular teeth.
They marked a certain position in society.

Hiram Ellsworth had been persuaded by his wife
That his position demanded new dental equipment.
After years of chewing sidewise like a cow
And soaking his bread in his coffee
He found his store teeth very uncomfortable.
He took them out whenever his wife was away.

One evening when she'd gone over the mountain
To visit their daughter
Hiram was sitting with some cronies
Around the stove in Brayley's store.
He was chewing tobacco,
Bringing his lower jaw up
So his chin almost hit his nose.
He'd left the new teeth at home.

"Jest how d'you like them store teeth, Hiram?"
Brayley drew up his arm-chair.
Hiram dropped his chair onto its four legs.

"I'll tell ye, Brayley,
I don't think nothin' of 'em.
If I'd 'a' bought me a sausage grinder
And screwed it onto the dinin' room table
I'd 'a' ben a durned sight better off."

Brayley's Steers

When Brayley ran the store
Down at the Borough,
He took in all sorts of things
In trade for store goods.

The Parkers had run up quite a bill,
And being very short of cash,
They offered Brayley
A pair of young steers
To settle their account.
He took the steers.
He'd kept them in the barn
For about a week
When Ira Barker came around.
He usually showed up when he had a thirst.
He did odd jobs for the storekeeper
And took rum for his pay.

Brayley was sitting on a high stool
Writing up his books
When Ira came in.
He shoved his glasses back
And said, "H'are ye."
Ira sat down on a nail keg
And lit his pipe.
"Wish you'd take them steers out
And draw me down a little wood.
I got some cut above the turn."
Brayley, acting as though it was settled,

Adjusted his glasses and went at his books.
Then, as an afterthought, he added:
"I'll give ye a gallon o' rum."

Ira thought for a minute.
Then he demanded the rum.
He'd heard about those steers.
Brayley shook his head.
"I'll give ye the rum when y' git back."
"I reckon, Brayley, I'll take the rum fust,
Afore I tackle them steers.
Life's too all-fired unsartin," he sighed.

The Hired Man

He was generally known as "Old Joe."
He'd drifted into town one spring
And hired out to Abel Williams.
That was some twenty years ago.

Old Joe was a good worker
But he couldn't stand prosperity.
Every time he got paid off
He would go on a spree for several days.
Finally Abel worked out a scheme
To keep Joe safe from temptation.
He kept him in clothes and tobacco
And gave him shelter and food.
Sometimes he gave him extra spending money,
At Fair time or Christmas.
The rest he put in the bank for him.
That was what he said he did.
Joe was getting old
And he was thankful for a home,
Though he frequently vowed he wouldn't stand it,
Not for another minute.

Joe was putting on his slippers in the kitchen.
He held up his shoe so the light struck it.
"Wal, Abel, I reckon you'd better git me
A new pair o' shoes tomorrer.
These are 'bout gone."
Abel looked over his paper.
"Gosh all firelock, it ain't more'n

Two months sence I got you them."
He dropped the paper and took off his glasses.
"You've had three pair sence I had one."
Joe dropped the shoe on the floor.
"Yes, Abel Williams, mebbe I hev,
But whilst I've ben awearin' them shoes out,
You've hed three new seats set into your briches."

The Last Wrong

Everybody said it was 'Liza
That made the Morgan farm pay.
Hiram was too easy-going.
He never made a cent
Until after he had married 'Liza.
She assumed command the day
Hiram brought her, a bride, to the farm.
In less than a week
The house looked like a different place.
Of course Hiram, living there alone,
Hadn't paid much attention to things.
Gradually she extended her field of action.
She was "pizen neat" and she drove Hiram
Until he had very little will of his own left.
The account in the Savings Bank grew
As Hiram's joy in life lessened.
Then he had a shock.

The Doctor had said he might last a week or a year.
He'd seemed to improve a little,
Then he just lay there, helpless.
Toward spring he seemed better
And during the summer he was able to walk a little.
But now he was down again and very feeble.

'Liza agreed with the Doctor
That it was only a question of a few hours.
Hiram had been asleep much of the time
For nearly a week.

'Liza was getting ready.
There would be extra folks to feed—
Hiram had a lot of relatives—
And she was getting things cooked ahead.
She heard a feeble call from the bed-room.
She hurried in still holding the fork
She'd been turning the ham with.
"Lizy," Hiram said in almost a whisper,
"I reckon mebbe I might relish
A small slice o' that ham I smelt cookin'."
'Liza poked the pillow and turned toward the kitchen.
"No, Pa, I ain't a-going t' cut that ham now.
It's fer a funeral."

Schooling

Caleb Potter was never cut out to be a farmer.
After his father died and he had the farm,
He more and more realized that a sense
Of filial duty had put him where he didn't belong.
His few terms at Burr Seminary,
Where his father thought his time was wasted,
Had given him glimpses of new worlds.
He made up his mind if he had children
They should have the chances he had missed.

He was plowing his south pasture.
From there he could see the length of the valley.
Down it each morning his two boys went
To the school whose white cupola
Stood out against the green of the mountains.
He and his wife skimped and saved
To send them there.
Ned, the older, seemed to understand.
He was getting what his father had missed.
It was carefree Bert who tried them.
He and his father didn't get along.

In the horse barn Caleb had two colts.
They were thoroughbreds and he planned
That some day they would bring the cash
To start the two boys in college.
He halter-broke them in the winter,
And now each day he drove them
On a two-wheeled rattling cart.

They were as different as his two boys.
What worked with one failed with the other.

As he rested at the end of the furrow
He was thinking of the boys.
Suddenly it came to him;
He'd been trying to train them both the same way.
When they were as different as Nip and Tuck,
The two colts.
That was why he'd failed to get at Bert.
He made up his mind he'd try another way.

Years later, when the boys had had
All the things he'd planned for them
He often said: "Mebbe those colts did pay
For those boys schoolin',
But they eddicated me besides."

Educated

Johnny had been to school
Since he was five.
He had sat on the front bench
Before his feet reached the floor.
As he grew taller
He moved back to the higher benches.

Being tall for his age, at twelve,
He found the back benches
Cramping for his long legs,
Which outgrew his pants
Just as his arms outgrew his shirt sleeves.

He had learned to write
But only with painful effort.
He always followed the strokes of his pen
With his tongue.
He could cipher fairly well
But his performance in the Fifth Reader
Was not very distinguished.
He read in a monotone
Stressing "ands" and "the's."

When he was thirteen he rebelled at school.
The teacher argued to no avail.
He refused to spend any more time on books.
His brother Elias was doing a man's work
And he was bigger.
He was reminded of great men

Who had valued learning above all else.
"No, sir. I don't care—
I know most as much as Elias,
And Elias knows most as much as Pa."
He raised his voice as he went on:
"And Pa knows enough fer anybody."

Gall

Dr. Stevens was attending Mrs. Simpson
Down on the river road.
She'd broken her hip in the late winter.
Henry Appleton lived on the farm this side.
He and his wife had raised two children
And succeeded pretty well with the farm.
Mrs. Appleton's tongue had been busy
Correcting the children when they were small.
It seemed to grow sharper after they left home
Ana she exercised it on Henry.
He got so he spent as much time as he could
Away from the house.

One morning he was taking the milk
To the cheese factory in the village.
As he jogged down the road
He met Dr. Stevens in his gig
Going out to see old lady Simpson.

Henry pulled up and stopped the Doctor.
He talked about things in general
And then asked the Doctor to call at his house.
"I reckon the woman's ailin'.
Nothin' serious but you better drop in."

Later in the morning Henry was going home
And he met the Doctor coming back to the village.
"Say, Henry," he turned on the seat of his gig,
"Your wife says you must be going crazy.

Says she never felt better in her life."
Henry flicked the dust with his whip.
"What'd you think ailed her, Henry?"

Henry raised his eyes.
"I'll tell ye, Doc.
When I come away this mornin'
There was a stream of the bitt'rest words
I ever heered, a-comin' out of that woman's mouth."
He gathered up the reins.
"I figgered she must be sufferin'
From an overflow o' the gall bladder."

A Division of Labor

Clarence was carrying on
The Orvis farm that year.
When the new owners had taken it over
The fences were in bad shape.
Clarence had discovered that
When he turned the young cattle
Into the upper pasture.

Henry Purdy, who lived on the next farm,
Had neglected his fences too,
So Clarence got him out one morning
To go along the line fence.
It took longer than it needed to
Because Henry would stop
To point out a likely clump of young pines
Which he took pride in;
As though he, instead of chance winds,
Was responsible for their planting.
Then he liked to tell about the marble
He felt sure lay under the pasture.
It was noon before they had gone over the fences
And found what needed to be done.
Clarence planned to do his part
That afternoon.
He'd finish it before chore-time.
Henry, whose efforts at farming
Were largely in his mind,
Looked at Clarence tolerantly.
Then he spoke in full round tones

As though he were delivering a weighty judgment.
"Well, Clarence, I planned
That we should undertake this work
On a partnership basis, working together . . ."
Clarence scratched his head.
"No, Henry. I reckon that'd make it
That I'd do nine-tenths of the work."
Henry drew himself up and spoke with dignity.
"No, Clarence, you are mistaken.
I estimate that my mental talents
Put up against your brute strength
Would make the division of labor
About equal."

Granting Permission

Holly was tall and lank.
His mustache was a faded red.
It drooped at the ends.
He came from the other side of the mountain.
Over there the down-east Yankees
And the Connecticut cousins
Must have mixed with folks from the Bay State.
Their way of talking leaves out the "r's"
And there is no such ending as "ing."
They seem to do most of their talking
In the roof of the mouth.

Holly was raking stones from the road.
It was a hot day
And Holly took off his drooping straw hat
And wiped his brow.
As he stepped out of the road
To let a car pass,
There was a screeching of brakes
And the car stopped
A few steps up the road.
A man stuck his head out of the window.
As Holly walked toward him,
He said in a patronizing tone:
"My man, we want to go to Rutland."

Holly's blue eyes shone.
He relaxed and thought a moment.
"Well, suh,

I don't think
I've got a mite of objection to it."
He started to go, then added:
"Only I'd a little rathah
You'd get back befoah dahk."

A Fire Extinguisher

Hiram Jones had some wood to sell.
The winter before a lumber company
Had cut several acres of timber
On a piece of mountain land he owned.
It was mostly white birch
And Hiram had dragged the tops down
And spent most of the fall
Cutting them up into stove wood.
It had stood out part of the winter
And all summer so it was well seasoned.

He had got rid of most of it
When Deacon Judson, who was nearsighted,
Came to his farm to order a few cords.
The little there was was getting spalty
But the Deacon didn't notice it.
He agreed to take two cords.

A week or so after he had delivered the wood
Hiram met the Deacon in the Post Office.
He would have avoided the meeting
If he'd seen the Deacon in time.
"Hwarye, Hiram," said the Deacon,
Peering at him through his thick spectacles.
"You're jest the man I wanted t' see."
Hiram, who still had some traces of conscience left,
Wished he hadn't gone for the mail just then.
"Hev you got another cord of that wood?"
Hiram, much relieved, thought he might find

Another cord scattered around the place.
The Deacon squinted.
"I figger I cud use jest about one more cord.
I got a contract t' put out the fires o' Hell
And I reckon one more cord of that wood
'Ud jest do the trick."

Dog's Ears

Mrs. William Sanderson of New York
Had bought a farm outside of the village.
She planned to retire to it to recuperate
After her winter's efforts to reform the world.
She reformed the farm into a summer place.
Then she began to notice things in the village
Which were badly managed.
When she was not busy instructing Jed Hall
How to build roads and keep them built,
She was telling the wives of the men on her place
How they should bring up their children.

Elias Parsons lived back on the mountain.
He always kept no less than five dogs.
They were mostly hounds
And during the summer they ranged the valley.
Mrs. Sanderson had been annoyed by them
And had complained to the Selectmen.
Getting no action from them
She decided to go directly to Elias.

She found him sitting in a chair
Propped against the front of his house.
The yard was strewn with bones.
She was greeted with a chorus of yelps
Mixed with admonitions from Elias,
Who did not bother to rise.
Wishing to be diplomatic, she spoke first
Of dogs in general and of her love for them.

Then she spoke of hounds
And of their unpleasant looks.
"Why is it, Mr. Parsons, that hounds
Always have such outlandish-looking long ears?"
Elias stroked the offending member of a lean hound.
"Wal, I didn't never see à hound
That wa'n't so equipped, Miss.
I allays figgered it helped
When they was arunnin' game.
Them ears gits to floppin' as they runs.
That fans th' air up and down
And blows the scent up inter their noses."
He let the chair down onto four legs.
"Leastwise that's th' way I figgers it."

A Mighty Hunter

Elias had been a mighty hunter.
He had never had less than five dogs
And he had always been correspondingly poor.
One of his pack had been his favorite.
She was a liver color and white hound.
She always looked as though
She was about to burst into tears.

One day Elias was sitting on his porch
Telling some young fellows
Of the exploits of his famous hound Sniff.
His tired eyes grew bright
With visions of the past.
He was so crippled with "rheumatiz"
That he could hardly move from his chair.
His name was in the Overseer's report
That came out each March.

"Yessir, I was fodderin' the cattle one day
When old Sniff was in her prime.
I'd heerd her runnin' a fox
Way up on them ledges up back.
She come nearer and nearer.
I went out front here jest in time
To see 'em comin' acrost that medder."
He leaned forward and pointed with his cane.
"That hound took that fox right down
Past them spruces and then turned south.
Well, sir, it was nip and tuck

When they went over th' hill there,
With that hound a leetle mite in th' lead
If anythin'."
He settled back in his chair
Worn out with the excitement of the chase.

Home

He lived in a one-roomed shack
In a clearing up on the mountain.
He'd gone up there years before
And cleared the land himself.
If he had any relatives
Nobody knew it.
He was getting old and feeble.
His one cow was poor
And his chickens were a sorry lot.
Once a week he walked to the village
And bought a few groceries
And his supply of tobacco.
His hair was long
And his clothes patched and dirty.

One fall the minister's wife called on him.
She was shocked at the way he lived.
She felt it wasn't safe
For him to be up there alone another winter.
He might be sick and die
And nobody would know until it was too late.
She tried to get him to clean up
But he didn't take kindly to her efforts.
She brought him food once
But he refused to take it.

One afternoon she went up there
Determined to get him to move down near the village.
She'd found a family who would take him in

And she had funds to pay for his keep.
She argued with him about his health.
She pointed out the dangers of living alone
In the coming winter.
At last she came to the real point—
The thing that distressed her most.
"But, Mr. Benton, you're house is so dirty."
He looked at the floor, his head in his hands.
Finally he said in a sad voice:
"Yes, Miss, I know,
But y' see it's home dirt."

Fiddlers Crook

There's a sharp bend in the road
That goes through the notch in the mountain.
There Jimmy, the fiddler, used to sit
On an old log hour after hour.
He lived with his folks just over the ridge.
They thought spending his time
At the bend with his fiddle
Was just another of his queer notions.
Day after day he sat there
Trying to make his fiddle tell things;
Things the brook said to him,
And the birds and the woods.
Somehow he could never make the fiddle tell.

It was Christmas night and the dance was over.
Jimmy was putting his fiddle away in its black box.
He had miles to walk and the night was cold
And the snow was getting deeper and drifting.
A stranger came up and asked to try the fiddle.
Reluctantly Jimmy let him take it.
He tuned it.
He began to play softly.
Then a miracle!
The old fiddle was telling.
It sang the songs of the birds;
It exulted with the brook, mad with spring;
It crooned the evening song of the wind in the spruces;
All of the things Jimmy had tried to coax from it
On the log at the bend in the Notch Road.

He went up the valley through the cold night.
As he climbed the mountain weariness overcame him.
He stumbled through the deep drifts.
He fell.
He must get to the old log at the bend in the road;
Then he could rest.

How comfortable it was there in the soft snow,
Beside the half-buried log.
Now he could rest.
The stars glistened in the cold blue of the Christmas sky.
He heard rushing brooks, just as the fiddle had told.
They grew fainter . . . fainter.
Birds were singing away off in the deep woods;
Fainter . . . fainter.
The cutting wind droned through the spruces;
Fainter . . . fainter.
It piled the snow over the old log;
Deeper . . . deeper.
There was a white mound beside it.

That's why they call the bend in the Notch Road
"Fiddlers Crook."

Plowing Time

The line of men moved slowly up the street.
It was too long for him to see either end,
But somewhere up there there was bread
And black coffee.
That would be worth the three hours' waiting.

A second-hand store spilled its drab wares
Through a disorderly doorway and onto the pavement.
As the line stopped before its dirty windows
His eyes brightened.
There, propped against a pile of dusty books,
Was a picture in a dusty frame:
A picture of a man plowing on a sunny hillside.

The morning breeze brought smells of growing things.
There were spots of green grass
Mixed with brown patches matted by winter.
He drove the team to the pasture bars.
Across the lowlands the turf was soft.
In the swampy places he could hear the suck of the soil.
He went on up the hill.

He hitched the team to the plow.
Around the lessening piece of green
He turned the rich brown furrows.
He stopped to watch the crows flying over the hill.
He could hear the shouts of children
Playing around the schoolhouse in the valley.
Away off a train whistled. It came nearer.

As he started the team again
A woodchuck scuttled for cover.
The next time he came around it was watching him
From the pile of dirt by its hole.

The wind brought the long blast of the noon whistle
From the mill near the village.
He unhitched his team and went down.
He let them drink in the pasture brook.
He knelt down and drank too.
The cold water hurt his throat.
As he passed the open kitchen door
He could smell the dinner cooking.
Two rhubarb pies were cooling
On a shelf by the kitchen window.

The line moved on.
Somewhere ahead there was bread
And a cup of black coffee.

The Wrestler

Deacon Amberson was sitting on his haunches
Reading a gay poster in the Post Office.
It seemed strange that he should be reading a show bill
When shows and dances were as bad as cards
The Deacon was nearing seventy.
He'd always lived up to his religious beliefs.
No matter how narrow the way
It had been straight.

He stood up and placed his glasses in a worn case.
"Going to the show, Deacon?"
He pointed to the bill.

WRESTLING
SOUTH LONDONDERRY

He clucked and gave his head a quick twist.
"Well, sir, if I was a few years younger
I'd rather go to that than anything I know of.
Yes, sir, I'd hitch up old Rattler and off we'd go.
Used to rastle some m'self."

One day when the Deacon was nearing sixty,
Thurber, the young blacksmith's helper,
And a stocky youth he was,
Had made remarks reflecting on old Rattler
The Deacon's horse.
Some words were passed and the Deacon, aroused to anger,
Threatened to put Thurber on his back.

Accepting the challenge the young smith
Got the surprise of his life.

The Deacon carefully placed his teeth on a shelf.
Then he grabbed Thurber.
Snap—and Thurber was on his back.
Claiming unpreparedness,
The Deacon let him get his hold
And flopped him again.
Then, shaking and out of breath,
He picked up his teeth and, bowing
To the astonished crowd, he went out.

Ed Bowers drew a long breath.
"By gosh, Thurber, the old man must 'a' kep' in practice
Wrastlin' with th' Lord."

A Guide Post

Hen got up from the store steps
And slouched over to the car.

"Dew I know how t' git t' Jericho?
Wal, I'd orter. Y' see the woman's folks
Come from over there.
Her sister's husband runs a blacksmith's shop
Right on the main street;
Does auto repairin' now they ain't much shoein'.
His name's Hawkins—Elmer Hawkins.
I ride over there every now and then
With Ike Loveland that runs the milk truck.
I—
Wal, I' acomin' t' that.
I'm jest tellin' ye sose you'll know
That I know what I'm talkin' 'bout.

"See that rud off yonder, branchin' from this?
That one t' the east thar?
How?
Lord, no, you don't take that one
'Less y' want t' go t' the Falls.
Take the left fork to th' west.
Foller that 'til ye come to a covered bridge.
Cross that and foller to th' left.
No, they ain't no other rud there.
Turn left as I was sayin', follerin' th' crick.
A mile er so down you'll come to a red barn.
It's new painted bein' a new barn.

Elmer Bump lives there.
He had t' build a new barn
On account of his old one havin' been burnt.
Pretty tough too.
Struck by lightnin'.
His wife—

"Yep. That rud goes right past that barn
And up over a hill t' a fork.
The right hand rud goes over to what they call
Th' Seventh Day neighborhood.
Ye see some forty-odd year ago—
Gosh, no. Not if y' want t' git t' Jericho.
Take the—
Wal, go it then.
If y' got a map why don't y' use it.
I got suthin' else t' do besides standin' here
Tellin' folks how t' git t' Jericho."

He shuffled back to his seat
On the store steps and lit his pipe.

No Harp Lessons

The Ladies of the Sewing Society
Had been satisfied for years to sit and sew.
They did have an annual meeting, and officers,
But most of the gatherings were informal.
They were held at the various houses of the members.
Usually, after an afternoon spent in work
Not unmixed with conversation, tea was served.

Maria Stock came to the meetings now and then.
Sewing seemed effeminate to her.
She was tall, gaunt, and weatherbeaten.
Her father used to say admiringly:
"Lord, Mari' had ought to been a man."
She was certainly mannish in look and action.
She felt the women should assert themselves.
Of course she was a leader in every reform idea.
The men of the town wished she had a man
And a large family. They might keep her too busy
To devote time to other people's affairs.
She had frequently tried to rouse the Sewing Society
To take some active part in temperance reform.
They always listened to her respectfully
And then usually voted five dollars.

She had been helping set up a quilting frame
At one of the fall meetings.
She did not join in the talk.
It was apparent that she had something on her mind.
There was a lull in the conversation

And Maria took off her spectacles and began to speak.
Gradually the talk in the different groups subsided.
Something in her manner always demanded a hearing.
She complained about the time wasted at their meetings.
She didn't deny that the sewing and quilting were good.
What she felt was that they should listen to something
While they were working, and even discuss it.
Finally she brought out her newest interest.
She felt they should be getting ready for the vote.
It was coming as sure as preaching
And she felt it would be wise
To take up the study of Parliamentary Law.

Ellen Swift, who always expressed her mind,
Even to Maria, put her sewing down in her lap.
She was violently opposed to woman's suffrage.
She looked over her glasses at Maria.
"I don't propose to waste my time on any such stuff."
She looked around for general approval.
Seeing she had it, she picked up her sewing again.
Then she added, as she threaded her needle:
"I figger on playin' a harp some day
But I ain't agoin' to waste time
Practicin' now."

Soda Water

He was taking her to the County Fair.
Except for the time she'd gone to court
When they sent her brother up to Windsor,
She had never been outside her mountain hamlet.

Along in the summer Sid began
By seeing her home from afternoon service
In the school-house, across from the mill.
He'd sit for a while and talk
Addressing most of his remarks to her father.
And now he was taking her to the Fair!

They stopped at a tent where a soda fountain
Was pouring forth a stream of foaming drinks.
"Come on, folks. Anythin' y' want—
Strawberry, Rawsberry, Anyberry, and Don't Care."
With his lady on his arm, Sid edged up to the counter.
"What kind you want?"
She shook her head. "Don't want none."
"Yes, y' do too."
"I don't, neither."
Turning to the dispenser with a worldly air he said:
"Gin her a glass and me too. Rawsberry."

He handed her the glass of pink foam.
She gazed at it, bewildered.
Turning her back so the dispenser shouldn't hear

She said in a strained whisper:
"What'll I do with it?"
He leaned close to her flushed face.
"Put it inside on ye."

Suffrage

The annual revival was on at Moller Hollow.
Heaven knows, they needed reviving.
It used to be a live place
When the chair factory was running.
After it burned, everything had gone to seed.
Most of the folks left there
Were too old to move, or too poor.
Once a year a week of meetings
Led by an old-time exhorter from over the mountain,
Was all the excitement the old place knew.

Ted Stiles wandered in to the meeting
To get out of the bitter cold.
He was enough "lickered up" to fall fast asleep
As soon as he sat down by the roaring chunk stove.
Through song and exhortation
He rested quietly.
Reaching his climax the preacher asked
Those who wished to go to heaven to rise.
They arose to a man, except Ted Stiles.
He woke to the noise of shuffling feet
And as they sat down he prepared to rise.
Seeing one black sheep in the flock
The preacher asked those
Who wished to go to hell to rise.
By then Ted had struggled to his feet.
Bewildered he looked around at the shocked faces.
Then, turning to the preacher,

227

He said in a thick voice:
"I ain't jest shirtin what 'tis we're votin' on
But me and you, parshen,
Sheem t' be 'n hopelesh m'nority."

Salt of the Earth

Josiah Webber and his wife live up the road
In that hospitable farmhouse.
Their seven children are all married except Jane.
It looks as though she might cling to the parent stem.
Tom, the youngest, lives with his wife and boys,
The second farm beyond the turn, on the hill.
All the rest of the children have gone away.

Josiah and his wife came from Winhall way.
She'd been a school teacher before she married.
They started on a small place Josiah had inherited.
Josiah's wife was a good business woman.
They managed to save a little money,
And after their second child was born they bought this
    place.
As soon as the children were able to get around
Each one had regular chores to do.
Ella was a splendid manager and Josiah did his share.
He was proud of her and boasts about her now.

They are pretty comfortably fixed,
And Ella and Josiah are willing to enjoy their leisure.
On a Sunday afternoon in summer
You'll find them sitting on the porch
With some of the grandchildren playing around.
Ella has more time to enjoy her grandchildren
Than she did her own.
She says she can enjoy them without being responsible
For all that they do.

She jokes Josiah sometimes
About the way she used to make him work.
"Yes," she'll say, nodding toward Josiah,
"All his folks were the salt of the earth,
And Josiah had his share of it too."
Then she'll assume the air of a penitent sinner.
"But I declare, livin' with me, for forty-odd years,
Has dissolved most of it out of him."

Their Day of Glory

It was the Fourth of July.
John and his friend Marcius
Were marching sedately up the street,
Playing martial music.
They were bedecked with small flags.
Each had on his shoulders home-made epaulets
And they wore sashes of faded red stuff.
Two ill-fitting hats of the Civil War
Completed their uniforms.

John was tall and lean.
He stepped high as though he might trip.
His faded eyes looked over square spectacles
And his mouth hung open.
He played an harmonica tied to a shingle,
Stuck in the front of his buttoned coat.
At the same time he sawed vigorously
On his beloved fiddle.

Marcius was short and stocky.
His gait was rolling like a sailor's.
He tried to appear a man of the world
But his blue eyes gave him away.
They rolled from side to side
As he played his harmonica,
And beat an irregular time with a small bell.

People came out from the houses on the village street
And now and then someone gave them money.

They accepted this with silent dignity,
Not as a gratuity but as something due artists.
If a child brought out a penny
John would make a courtly bow
And, stooping, he'd kiss the hand of the donor.

Arriving at the village store
They would lay in a stock of tobacco.
Perhaps John would get a new harmonica.
Marcius always knew of a patent medicine he wanted to
    try.
They drank soda water and smoked cigars.
The Tavern keeper gave them lunch
While they sat in rocking chairs on the porch.
Then they played a grand finale
And John, in his exuberance,
Danced a clog.

As the shadows were closing in on the valley
Down the river road, two tired old men
Trudged in silence through the dust,
Going back home—
To the Poor Farm.

The Valley Road

He had traveled the valley road for years.
On foot, on horseback, in all kinds of wagons;
Then on a bicycle and now in an automobile.
He'd known every foot of the highway intimately
And yet, somehow, this morning it was different.
Maybe it was the clear·light of a sun
Seen earlier than in recent years
That made him see things he hadn't noticed.
Probably it was something inside stirred by the new day.
He remembered how his father had gone over that road
Hundreds of times on all sorts of errands to the village.
Perhaps he, too, on some clear clean morning like this
Had let his horse walk while *he* remembered
How *his* father and grandfather, too—
How they'd all gone up this road from the farm to the
    village.
They had all seen those same Green Mountains
As he saw them this morning.

He tried to think of the changing times
That those generations marked.
He wondered what might have brought them out
Perhaps on a cold winter night
When the snow creaked under the runners,
Going to the village to sit with a sick relative
Or probably most often going to the Meeting House
Maybe for prayer meeting or something to do with politics.
No doubt the younger ones had been hurrying to some
    dance

Or a supper or likely the younger men to make a special
   call.
He remembered the uncle who had gone up that road
Dressed in an ill-fitting uniform
To join his comrades and take the train South—
A one-way trip for him.
Yes, and all but that one had made their last trip
From the valley farm to the burying ground in the village.
He passed the one-room schoolhouse still standing.
He drove under the old elm with its high arching branches
Under whose shade the generations had eaten the noonday
   lunch.
Somehow that road, that cool clean morning,
Seemed to carry the whole of life's story—
Its joys and sorrows; the small things of everyday
And all the moving pageant of history, too,
Seen by the men and women and the boys and girls
Of four generations who had lived on the valley farm.

An old road like the valley road that goes to the village
Makes neighbors of the long ago and the here and now.
They always said it was two miles to the village.
On that clean cool morning it was four generations.

III

BACK COUNTRY

City Ignorance

For some time there had been grumbling
Among the more active members of the church.
They had tried not to be too outspoken
But among themselves they got more and more
Critical of the minister's wife.
Her attitude wouldn't have been so unfortunate
If she hadn't been a good six inches
Taller and much heavier than her husband.
To make up somewhat for his handicap
The Reverend Silas walked with soldierly bearing
With his chest out to such an extent
That he had a backward curvature of the spine.
All these unfortunate physical differences
Might have gone overlooked with now and then a smile,
But Mrs. Silas turned out to be the dominant one.
Of course as time went on she was considered plain
     "bossy."
While she might refrain from public expression
When some decision was demanded of her husband,
He usually managed to get her opinion
Before finding that he agreed with her fully.

What brought matters to a head was a conference
A Committee of Deacons held in the front
Of the double parlor one evening.
The doors into the back parlor were carefully shut
By Deacon Hanover before he sat down.
Finally it became necessary for the Reverend Silas

To express his opinion and he stepped to the double
    doors.
"Just a minute," he said carefully pushing on one of
    them.
His attempt to open it just enough to slip through
Met with opposition which turned out to be
An ear attached to the head of his helpmate.

That autumn a young bachelor from the city
Was keeping house for himself in the parsonage.
He had been there several months when Abbie
    Stompkins
Electrified the semi-weekly sewing meeting
By remarking that the Reverend had a companion.
In the silence she slowly spoke of the young man's
    virtues.
"Not a word have I heard against him.
But what does he do now but go to the city,
    mind you,
And come back with," she paused a dramatic
    moment . . . .
"With a female cat that he paid fifty cents for,
And the town here overrun with kittens free for the
    takin'."

Frugality

The Grange supper had been well attended
And while the womenfolk cleared the tables
And washed the dishes in the kitchen
The men gathered around the heater
In the far corner of the dining room.
The February sun had already begun
To warm things up in the middle of the day
Even when the mercury dropped to zero at night.
It was this sign of relenting
Which had brought out many who for weeks
Had been winterbound even though snow and ice
Were still holding most of the landscape.

Naturally the men had got around
To preparations for the first spring operation
On most of the farms on the hills, sugaring.
There were still some who were skeptical
About the new boiling apparatus, the Evaporator,
Which it was claimed produced better syrup
Than the long used open pans.
More than likely the lack of money
Kept some from giving up the old method.
That was not a factor in Eben Wool's stern criticism.
It was generally agreed that he took the prize
As the best off and tightest man in town.
He was loud in his denunciation
Of the new method of boiling and of the product.
Not wasting any cash on such things as the Grange
He often served as a target for special criticism.

239

As frequently, this night he was dragged in
And examples of his stinginess recounted.
Finally Judge Hallowell smiled and asked,
"Did I ever tell you of the time I observed Eben
At the moment he discovered a mouse
That had perished by drowning in a bucket of sap?"
He paused and chuckled and then went on;
"Well, I presume he's the only man
Who would have ever taken the pains
To wring that mouse out before throwing it away."

Evie, Notion Peddler

Until she was over seventy
Evie was a familiar figure in the village
And, when the going was not too bad,
For several miles outside.
She always lugged a canvas telescope bag
Which seemed too much for her short plump body.
In it there was an amazing collection of "notions"—
Thread, and needles, and buttons, and tape,
And all things home-sewing housewives needed
To keep the family wardrobe in useful condition.
It might be that Evie made more of her burden
When she was outside where any passing vehicle
Would be sure to pick her up.
It is probable, too, that about dinner time,
Or in the summer at supper time,
Her arrival at certain customers' homes
Was not quite the happenchance she made it seem.

It was true that after the evening meal
Some of the menfolks would happen
To be going to the village on some errand.
"Get your duds together, Evie, and come along,"
    he'd say.
In most of the homes, especially outside the village,
Evie's visits were looked forward to.
She was one of the few breaths of outside air
And the one connection with the life in the village.
The infrequent times when some bad storm

Made her an unexpected overnight guest,
Gave the hosts a grand chance to catch up on local
  events.
These away-from-home nights were few
Mostly because of Moses, her large black tom cat.
She'd worry about Moses and wonder about him
Until she unlocked her door next day
And heard his welcoming voice.

One day she'd stopped at the Holden farm
And been quite surprised to find it was dinnertime.
She'd more than paid for that generous meal
By divulging the fact that one of the village people
Had fallen heir to five thousand dollars.
The whole story was gone over in detail
As to the worthiness of the heir and mostly
What she would do with so much wealth.
"What would you do, Evie, if you had five thousand
Handed out to you?"
Evie sat back, her knife and fork in hand.
Finally she said decidedly: "There's one thing sure.
They's a few folks I'd snub good and proper!"

A Real Fish Catcher

If there was one rule of living
Which Ike Morton always lived up to it was
Never to allow his business to interfere with his fishing.
Probably most people came to believe
That from the opening day in May
To the sad last day of the season in September,
Fishing was Ike's chief business.
Hardly a day passed that at some time or other
Ike could not be found fishing in the Battenkill.
On days when others found it too cold or too wet
Ike, well bundled up in ragged coats,

Might be found up to his waist in the chilly water.
He knew every twist and turn from the red bridge—
The one east of the village—to the other one,
Three miles down the valley.
He knew where the good holes were for certain hours
And just how to place his bait
So it would be carried to the feeding spot.
He could fish with a fly and often did,
In late summer when the water was lower.
But he really enjoyed the old barnyard hackle more.

He not only kept his family in fish
But he had several friends who made it worth his while
To make sure they had a mess
When they had guests in for dinner.
Often his sure catch saved their own reputations
Which they had built up with the visitors.

Their morning's efforts might have had meager results
But Ike could always be relied on to help out.

One day one of the men who were helping
On a newcomer's summer place
Was getting in a little rest from his labor
By discussing fishing with his employer.
He was telling about Ike's prowess with hook and line.
As the newcomer slowly tore himself away
The man took his weight off the rake handle, saying,
"Yessir, when it comes t' fishin' Ike Morton beats all.
By judast, I believe that feller could catch trouts
Out 'a bowl o' oatmeal, by judast!"

Statehouse Bound

Probably if she had lived
Some years later
Mrs. Baker would herself have run for office.
Certainly Eben would have been contented
To go on in a puttering way
Running the small farm
Just as his father had done,
But his wife mistook her own ambition
For hidden talents in Eben.
She was determined to remove the napkin.

Through her efforts he ran for Grand Juror.
He was elected to her satisfaction.
He was the only candidate.
Once in, she made him do some things
He alone would have overlooked.
Then when three candidates served notice
That they were ready to serve as town representative,
Eben's wife decided in the mixup
Her husband's talents might be recognized.
To everybody's amazement, except his wife's,
Eben was elected by a slim margin.
Mrs. Baker's elation grew less high
When she suddenly realized
That she would not be at her husband's elbow
To see that he made the right decisions
Away off there in Montpelier.

At last the day of departure came.

Eben was clad in a new suit of store clothes
Which had evidently not been modeled
By anyone possessing his physical characteristics,
And obviously his new shoes
Had not been broken in.
As Eben stumbled up the steps of the impatient train
Dragging his overstuffed telescope bag,
His wife stopped him for a moment
For a last-minute load of advice.
As he started on, her parting words were:
"And you jest remember, Eben Baker,
Don't you be awearin' those go-to-meetin' clothes
Too common."

Cake and Character

If there was anything stirring in the village
Which demanded workers
Emily Strabridge could always be relied on
To pitch in and help
If she was approached in the right way.
It was always advisable also
To see to it that the right person
Brought the matter to her attention.
Her agreeing to do what she could
Never was any assurance that her interest
Was wholeheartedly enlisted.
She was always bound to find some reason
To criticize the people backing the undertaking
And usually there was something wrong
With the way it was being run.

If anyone ever ventured to praise another
Emily's mouth would become a straight line
And when she had a chance she'd bring out something
To show the praise wasn't fully warranted.
She always prided herself on being strictly honest.
She was convinced that nobody was perfect.
So when anybody offered a candidate for that condition
Honesty demanded the discovery of some flaw.
Strangers were always objects of suspicion
And had to prove themselves before acceptance.
Withal, Emily was such a hard worker
That those who knew her just ignored
Her habitual discovery of imperfections in her fellows.

One night there was a Grange supper
And as usual Emily had been asked to furnish.
As usual she had brought up several matters
Which she felt called on to criticize
In the way the Grange was being run
Before she agreed to furnish a cake for the supper.
She always made one kind of cake—
A white loaf cake with dried currants scattered
     through it.
Some of the younger element called it "Em's fly cake."
When it was placed on the table one of the men
Who recognized Emily's handiwork,
Said to another, speaking behind his hand,
"You can easily understand Em's making that kind
     of cake,
Knowing what a lot of flies she's always finding
In the ointment."

Lucky

There had been considerable talk
Around the village about the goings on
At the old Johnson place north of the crossroads.
A man and his wife had bought it through an agent.
They had moved in bag and baggage in February
And the report was they were setting up a "chicken
  ranch."
The few who had met the two
Said they seemed real pleasant—not a mite citified
Though they were supposed to be right from New York.

Some of the people remembered when the hen house
A long low building near the road had been built
By the son of a former owner of the Johnson place.
He'd sunk quite a bit of money trying to raise
Some fancy breed of Chinese chickens.
They had feathers on their legs.
The general verdict had been that the owner
Had feathers in his head.
They didn't know that Harry and Ellen Seeley
Had spent much of their spare time for several years
Studying the chicken business thoroughly.
Ellen had even taken a short course
In an Agriculture College after the children had grown
  up.
They were both thorough and systematic in all they did
And this new venture had not been undertaken lightly.
They tried out the brooders for days to be sure.
When the first lot of a thousand day olds came

Everything was ready for them, quarters and food.
As time went on they gave their charges
All of the scientific treatment to ward off disease.
The first few weeks they were up several times a night
To see that everything was going properly.

By late summer their flock which could be seen from
the road
Was accepted by the village as proof
That they knew what they were doing.
Henry Stoddard stopped one day by the edge of the
yard.
He told Harry he's always "had hens" on his farm
But generally he'd been unlucky raising them.
He'd found he got the best chicks when a hen stole
her nest.
He generally left as much to nature as possible.
Impressed, even though Harry's methods seemed
foolish,
He finally gathered up his reins and started off, saying!
"All's I can say, young man, is that
You folks have had an awful lot o' good luck."

At the Grist Mill

The old stone grist mill
Looked as though it had grown where it stood
A century or so ago between the hill and the river.
Its walls were two feet thick, solid masonry,
And in case of need it might have served
As a fort if such were ever needed
In that peaceful valley.

The water that turned the big wheel
Came from a small pond upstream
Flowing smoothly and quietly, with dignity,
Along its stone walled channel to the power maker.
There it poured in a mad torrent to its task.
There was always the rhythmic swish of the water
As each bucket of the overshot wheel
Emptied its load into the outlet channel below.
This might be drowned out by the rumble
Inside when the mill was busy with its grinding.
Then the miller had to shout to be heard above the
    roar.
Conversation with his customers generally went on
Outside on the loading platform in summer
And inside the office by the big stove in winter.
Everything was coated with fine white meal dust,
Including Scott Hibbard, the miller.
Several dusty cats were also part of the working force,
But daytimes they usually slept in the office.
They were the night watchmen.

One spring day Sam, the miller,
Saw Frank Monkton in his sagging buckboard
Driving toward the mill.
Frank was generally known as a dead beat.
His name was on the books of every store in town
And the miller had told Joe, his helper, not to trust him.
He stopped at the platform and swung his feet out.
He talked crops and weather and then casually:
"Better drop a hundred o' meal on for me."
He was reaching into his pocket
When Sam dropped the bag on the back of the
   buckboard.
"That'll be seventy-five cents," Sam said.
"Can you change a twenty?" Frank asked,
His hand was still in his inside pocket.
"Gosh, no" Sam said, taken aback.
His customer withdrew his hand and picked up the reins.
Clucking to the horse he said in parting:
"I was 'fraid y' couldn't,
So I didn't fetch it along."

A Tinkerer

Egbert Buckley had operated for many years
In what had started out to be a Blacksmith's Shop.
Egbert, as a young man had learned to do shoeing of
  a sort
By working with George Wissel, a real artist at it.
But Egbert didn't like horses and they knew it
So from the very start George knew
That his pupil would never make a real blacksmith.
He did discover that when it came to repair work,
Such as fixing a broken down wheel
Or splicing a broken pole or whiffletree
Egbert would spend hours and turn out a good job.

George also learned that Egbert was good at tinkering
Broken down household things like pumps;
And when the summer people introduced lawnmowers
He seemed to know just how to make them work.
It wasn't long before out back there were spare parts
For almost any piece of farm machinery.
Egbert had rescued them from broken down ones
Which were beyond repair.

After George Wissel died and cars had come in
Egbert had the yard filled with wrecks
And spent all his time fixing them up
With parts from this one and that.
He'd usually trade the new hybrid machine
For another wreck and get something to boot.
Meanwhile straight repair jobs were left waiting.

His house was built of old lumber he'd picked up
Usually from some tumbled-down building.
He might have to put in a new window frame
Or a new door but he was never happy about it.
Most of the furniture in the house
Was made up of odd pieces from cast off wrecks.
He'd spend hours working with a washing machine
He bought at an auction
And then have to keep tinkering on it every Monday,
Rather than finish up some paying job and buy a new
    machine.

In general Egbert looked as though he himself
Might have been made of cast off parts.
Even his eyes weren't mates—
One was blue and the other brown.

He was pulling over a pile of junked parts of many
    things
When somebody suggested he give up hunting,
And build something new from the start for a change.
Egbert straightened up and ran his hand through his
    bushy hair.
"Nope, I wa'n't ever much on new stuff," he said,
"But I'm all hell on fixin' things."

Uncle Sam Plays Cupid

The first thing in the chain of events
Which eventually led to the strange marriage
Of Eli Batterson was the arrival in town of an
  architect.
He was sent by the daughter of one of the old families
Who had married the riches of one of America's new
  families.
Her husband had made a fortune as a building
  contractor
And his wife had worked in his office.
It was after they'd been to the village
To bury her father and close up the old family
  farmhouse
That Millie Stubbs, now Mrs. Amerino, had told her
  husband
About the little library in the back of the Town Hall.
She pointed it out and laughed.
Her husband smiled and then he became thoughtful.

The upshot of it was the town was to have a library.
There was plenty of good limestone in the hills
And the architect found some easy to get
Back of Eli Batterson's sugar house.
By the time the library was built contractor Amerino
Had made a deal with Eli and a regular quarrying
  operation
Was getting out stone for various city buildings.
So for the first time Eli made the painful discovery
That there was such a thing as an income tax.
He had to get Judge Cannon to make the blank out
  for him

And the second year it was fairly large, in Eli's
    estimation.
And paying out had always been painful to him.
He lived alone, worked his small farm, and with the
    new riches
Instead of expanding he drew in tighter.
The Judge laughingly told him he should have a family.
He mentioned the exemptions children offered.
Even a wife would save him on his tax.

Eli was 46 and soon after the Judge's suggestion
It got noised abroad that he had married Maria
    Appleton,
A woman considerably older than he, who came to his
    house
And did cleaning once a week.
He'd taken her to the Methodist parsonage one evening.
When the ceremony was over he gave the minister
    five dollars.

A week or so later he rang the parsonage doorbell again.
He went into the Minister's study and without a word
He handed him another five dollar bill.
"But you already generously rewarded me," the
    Minister said.
Eli put his wallet back in his pocket and reached for
    his hat.
"Well, Reverend, y'see I got me a better bargain than
    I expected.
Found out yestiddy that my woman bein' over 65
Saves me another $600 on m' income tax, by jiminetty,
Makin' twelve hundred dollars on account of marryin'
    her.
Fair t' share it, ain't it, Reverend?"

Unlicensed

The usual number of fishermen,
For whom the first day of fishing is sacred,
Had been out in spite of the fact
That ice formed on their lines as well as on their
   whiskers.
Of course the catch was small, except for a few
Who always had a good mess ticketed
No matter what the weather.

It was three weeks later when a warm sun
Followed several days of showers.
The brooks were down from the spring excitement
And the temperature was kindly enough
To make it comfortable for the fisherman.
Milo Stevens had been out for several hours
And had landed five good sized fish as brook trout go.
What was more to his liking, he had landed them
Under very trying circumstances.
Most of all he had been using a fly for the first time.
Well satisfied with his afternoon's labor
He was walking down the road toward the village.

From another road came Willie Timpson.
He was carrying a good sized tin pail.
Milo waited for him to catch up.
He looked into the pail which was half full of fish.
"Good gracious!" He said hefting the pail.
"You must have considerable over the limit there."

Willie started along, saying he guessed not.

"Not only that, but unless my eyesight is failing

You've got several you'd have to stretch to make 'em
legal."

Willie plodded along saying nothing.

Finally Milo stopped, suggesting that Willie had better

Go home by a side road with a catch like that.

"Where'd you get 'em anyhow," he asked in a severe
tone.

Willie looked taken back and said meekly:

"Up in that brook that runs through the Heath place."

"Jeerusalem! You darned idiot. Don't you know that's
posted?

Been posted for three years and a sign on every tree."

Willie vowed he'd never noticed.

"Well you'd better notice. You'll be losing your license."

Willie looked puzzled; he thought a minute and then
asked

"What license?"

An Autumn Tour

Whenever he had any free time all summer
Henry was asking questions and gathering maps.
He was planning a vacation trip in the country.
He found just thinking of it on the hot days
When he sat at his bench in the shop
Eased the day's drudgery.
He imagined how it would feel
Driving along country roads, unhurried,
Breathing in the cool air of autumn.
He spent his evenings pouring over his road maps
And reading about tourist homes
In circulars he had gathered.

Sarah, his wife, didn't have much to say.
Now and then she asked a question but more often
She tried to cool Henry's ardor with doubts.
She had always said she was a home-body
And the more Henry talked of the trip as really coming
    off
The more she hoped something might come up to
    prevent.
Often, after Henry had spent an evening
Talking about what they'd see and where they'd go,
She'd lie awake wondering how she could ever
Get used to eating meals she hadn't cooked
Or how she could sleep in a bed she hadn't made.

As the day drew near she thought of more and more
    things

They'd have to take, but even a back seat
Piled high with things they wouldn't use,
Had no effect on Henry's happy enthusiasm.

In spite of everything on the day appointed
Sarah found herself leaving the noise and bustle
Of the friendly streets of home.
After a few hours they were gradually climbing
Following a brook which they crossed and recrossed.
Houses became fewer and then there were none.
When they reached the height of land Henry stopped.
There ahead the valley opened.
A warm haziness wove into a tapestry the autumn
    colors.
The only sounds were in the already fallen leaves
Where birds scratched or a squirrel hurried.
Henry sat silent while Nature's alchemy
Slowly freed him from the tensions of daily living.

Sarah looked around at the loneliness.
Suddenly she straightened up, and spoke with
    excitement.
"Henry! We've got to turn 'round and go straight back.
I forgot to put a note in the bottles
When I set 'em out for the milkman."

Companions

In spite of the fact that the Russ brothers
Had lived all their lives near enough to each other
So that hardly a day passed without a meeting,
They always enjoyed each other's company.
They were only a year apart in age.
And as boys growing up on the hill farm back of the
    village
They had been inseparable companions.
After they married and had separate homes
Each wife soon realized that she had not one
But two men to adjust her life to.

If the Russ brothers ever disagreed, as they doubtless
    did,
It was never known to the general public.
When they had each passed eighty-five
It was observed that they sometimes did argue
Usually about some event in the earlier days.
Some of the younger fry discovered this
And enjoyed getting them at it by asking some
    innocent question
On a matter of local history.

One day Edgar, just past his ninetieth birthday,
Drove back from the village in his Model T
And sat down on the porch to read the paper.
His granddaughter found him there slumped over in his
    chair.
When Frank, his younger brother was told

He took the news without saying a word.
He seemed suddenly to lose interest
And sat staring off into space much of the time.

The day after the funeral he agreed to go down the
    valley
With one of his sons who felt a change might help.
Gradually on the journey down the old man began to
    talk
But the whole burden of his conversation was his
    Loneliness.
His son called his attention to a contemporary.
"Ed Masters?" He spoke with some of his old fire.
"Good Lord. He's got softening of the brain.
Hasn't spoken a sensible word for at least three years.
Nice comforting companion he'd be."
The son tried again mentioning Samuel Hazen.
"Sam Hazen?" His father fairly snorted.
"He and I never did agree on anything anyhow
And since he had that shock he'd got less sense
Than he used to have if that's humanly possible."

Rather pleased at the show of spunk the son drove on
    in silence.
Finally the old man looked at him and smiled.
"I reckon I'll take up with that newest great grandson.
He's not getting through—he's just beginning."

A Good Reason

Steve Allister cared more for horses
Than he ever did for any human being.
He came naturally by his passion
Since his father raised them on the farm,
And Steve grew up hearing horse talk
From the time he was old enough to know
What the word meant.
He sat in his father's lap and "drove"
As soon as he could hold the reins.
By the time he was in his teens
He was helping break colts to harness and saddle
And his specialty came to be the tough ones.
He had a way with them just as his father had.

When he began going with Bess Talbot,
Who was equipped with black hair,
Snapping black eyes and a temper to match,
People decided he encountered the same challenge
He met and conquered in the wildest colts he tamed.
Several times during the period of courtship
They quarreled violently and for days
Were not on speaking terms.
Once a neighbor overheard their wild arguing
And she reported that their tongue-lashing ability
Seemed to be about equal, with Bess having more
    staying power.
Then, quite suddenly, they were married by the parson.

Perhaps, as the years passed

263

Their arguing didn't mean as much deep down,
But Bess found frequent things to berate her husband
    about
And Steve refused to take her talk in silence.

One day Steve drove up the hill in front of his house.
He had a heavy load of stone on the wagon
And his well-matched team of grays
Had to dig in and pull to get up the last steep pitch.
The Parson in his buggy waited by the gate
And Steve stopped his panting team across from him.
The Parson and Steve and Bess were long-time friends.
"Steve," the Parson began, "How well that pair pulls
    together."
Steve admitted they were well matched.
"Might be a sermon there," the Parson continued
    looking off to the hills.
Steve smiled at his old friend.
"Well, you see, Parson, the thing is
That pair there've got only one tongue between 'em."

Flood Control

Grandma Gordon was 91
When her son came home from the shop
Seven miles down the valley one night with news.
At last they were going to build the dam across their
   valley.
It was a flood control dam to save the towns
All down their valley and the valley of the bigger
   river
From ever again being the victims
Of the devastating destruction of nature uncontrolled.
To Grandma Gordon that seemed like large talk
Dealing with matters not meant for man's hand.

When the young men prowled around the valley
Peeking through their little brass tubes
It really meant little to her.
One of them pointed to a high hill
Where she'd picked wild strawberries
Ever since she was able to handle so small a thing
And to place it elsewhere than in her small mouth.
That, he said, would utterly disappear—
Moved miles down the valley to back the dam.
Grandma looked at the young man.
Moving mountains was a matter of faith
According to her engineering knowledge.

Before the lawyers came with papers to be signed,
Her son had made her understand that in time
Her farm would be flooded—her land a lake bottom.
The fertile land cleared by her forebears
Drowned forever.
And the house, a home for three generations
Built of timber cut from the surrounding acres,

Might be moved to land which never knew it.
To transplant it seemed as impossible to Grandma
As to uproot the ancient maples that stood before it.

Though the wicked waste of change
Smote Grandma Gordon's frugal soul,
She gradually seemed to accept it all.
Her home, her farm, the old life—
All this must be drowned to keep the new
From some far off time when nature might take over,
Destroying the valley with flooding waters.

Then came the auction when strange people
Tramped through the house and took away
The many things which made it home.
Through it all Grandma Gordon sat in her rocker
Greeting this friend and that stranger
Each with a smile which seemed to hide something.

The next day they took Grandma slowly down her
    valley
To the new town where in new surroundings
She'd find many things she'd always had around her.
She saw the great machines roaring like monsters
Making the land she's always known
Into something like the old pictures in the family Bible,
When God was forming the earth from chaos.
Those sleek yellow machines frightened Grandma.
Deep down she felt they were taking over
Powers that belonged only to God Almighty.
She trembled at the thought of the certain outcome
Of this growing struggle on the earth.
She found herself crossing on concrete bridges
Streams where there had been rumbling planks
Adding to the mystery of covered bridges.
Her son pointed out smoothed and level spots

266

Where weeks ago homes of her old friends had stood.
Perhaps further along they'd see one of them
Standing bleak and alone on its new hilltop.
"We'll come and see them all someday," he'd said.
Grandma listened to all the hopeful talk
And smiled with a sort of far off look in her eyes
As though she wasn't really there at all.

* * * *

They put her to bed that night
In the place which would never be her home;
For that night Grandma Gordon went away.